BUTTERFLIES

BUTTERFLIES

A comprehensive guide to this
beautiful insect species

Oceana

AN OCEANA BOOK

This book is produced by
Quantum Publishing Ltd.
6 Blundell Street
London N7 9BH

ISBN: 978-1-84573-263-9

QUMBUTT

Printed in Singapore by
Star Standard Industries (Pte) Ltd.

Contents

INTRODUCTION

Zebra

Mankind's appreciation and fascination with butterflies transcends recorded history. From the Bronze Age frescoes of Thebes to the Greek statue of Psyche, this insect has always been depicted in art. Be it the Monarch that decorated the ceremonial headdress of Chief Sitting Bull or the exquisite jade artwork of the Chou dynasty, Lepidoptera have always played a part in human life. These loveliest of creatures evoke only the happiest of memories to all who chance their way.

This book expresses the delight so many have for these blithe, beautiful beings using both superbly illustrated prints alongside photographs to enhance the text.

From egg to the emergence of an adult, the butterfly's life still holds many mysteries. Metamorphosis may never be fully understood. The pages that follow place equal importance on every stage of development in hopes of unlocking some clues to the mysteries. Many caterpillars are as beautiful as the adults and deserve equal presentation. Locating the golden ovum of a Zebra Longwing can be as exciting as witnessing the flight of a Giant Swallowtail.

Over the years, attitudes concerning butterflies and the collecting of them have changed. Lepidopterists have come a long way since the explorer A. S. Meek first collected Birdwing butterflies with the aid of the Papuan natives and their bows and arrows. Many species have become extinct, with many more added to the endangered list all the time. The destruction of habitat and the spraying of pesticides have taken their toll. However, there is hope for these fragile jewels. Butterfly consciousness has swept the world. Many conservationally minded naturalists realize that the enjoyment received from releasing a precious quarry outweighs the satisfaction of a full Riker mount. This is most evident today with the proliferation of butterfly zoos worldwide. Most lepidopterist societies have changed their focus from collecting butterflies to photographing and rearing them. And they have found that the challenge of the camera exceeds that of the net.

The reasons people become involved with Lepidoptera are often as varied as the unwitting souls who fall under their spell. It may be for scientific research, for photographic aspirations, or merely to idle away a summer afternoon. No matter what the reason, one thing is for certain: more important than the largest of nets is the smallest of books. Since before the Renaissance, early naturalists have compiled and used journals to assist them in their work. Such note taking is even more important today. With rapid land development and lightning-fast worldwide travel, butterfly populations can sometimes appear or disappear almost overnight. Harmful species can infest an area seemingly out of nowhere. Likewise, a specimen thought to be extinct may be rediscovered. This is why a good book that records the appearance, habitat, and habits of butterflies is a must. An amateur can be an excellent monitor of the natural world, but the purpose of his or her endeavor should not be to collect every species but to understand them.

Palamedes Swallowtail

Evolution of the butterfly

Our understanding of the evolution of butterflies is sketchy at best. This should come as no surprise when their relatively delicate composition is considered.

The most revealing specimens have been those few found encased in amber, which is the fossilized resin from ancient plants. The oldest of these have been dated to the Cretaceous period, about 100-140 million years ago. Fossil evidence suggests that this was the same period that saw the first flowering plants, including magnolia, beech, and fig.

Some researchers have suggested that the well-defined nature of these plants at that time points to a much earlier beginning in their development, perhaps as early as the Jurassic period more than 200 million years ago. Because much of the evolutionary development of flowering plants and the insects that feed on their nectar, and in turn spread their pollen, has been closely linked, this could also indicate an earlier butterfly ancestor.

Tracing the ancestry still further, we would eventually arrive at a segmented animal, quite similar to today's silverfish and springtails. This was probably the ancestor of all insects.

Order lepidoptera

Modern-day butterflies are members of the insect order Lepidoptera, a word that actually describes the presence of scales on their wings. It is derived from the Greek words lepis, for scale, and pteron, for wing. The order is further divided into superfamilies, two of which constitute those species that are the focus of this book: the true butterflies (Papilionoidea) and the skippers (Hesperiordea).

The body of the true butterfly is slender, while that of the skipper is thick and bulky. True butterfly wings are large and full by comparison, while skipper wings are proportionately smaller and triangular. In flight, the true butterfly may be swift but generally is not powerful. Its wing strokes are not so fast as to appear a blur. The skipper flies swiftly, often in a darting fashion and often with wings blurred.

While a basic knowledge of the differences between the two superfamilies is important to a thorough understanding of our topic, from this point we will use the word butterfly to cover both true butterflies and skippers.

The two superfamilies are further divided into 11 families, the members of each family bearing many similar characteristics. The families are Papilionidae—Swallowtails; Pieridae—Whites and Sulfurs; Lycaenidae—Gossamer-Winged; Riodinidae—Metalmarks; Nymphalidae—Brush-footed; Libytheidae—Snout; Danaidae—Monarchs; Satyridae—Satyrs and Wood Nymphs; Heliconiidae—Tropical Heliconians; Hesperiidae—True Skippers; and Megathymidae—Giant Skippers.

Such taxonomic divisions, continuing below the families into genus, species, and subspecies, are essential to scientific study of the animal kingdom. Linnaeus was the first to propose the current binomial, or two-name, system of subdivision in 1758 in his "Systema Naturae." Under this system each creature is identified by two Latin names, the first (beginning with a capital letter) is the genus and the second is the species. For example, the scientific name of the Comma is *Polygonia comma*.

Many changes have been made to Linnaeus' original scheme, and debate and rethinking of some classifications continues, but the binomial names of all animal life are precise and tend toward the necessary uniformity. Common names may seem more familiar and easier to use, but they can be unreliable and lead to the same butterfly being identified with several different names.

above: The taxonomic name of this hairstreak is Thecla

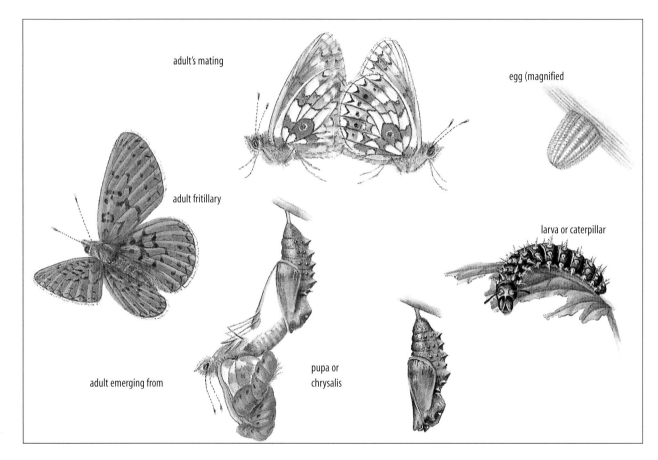

adult's mating

egg (magnified

adult fritillary

larva or caterpillar

adult emerging from

pupa or
chrysalis

**The life cycle of the
Silver-bordered Fritillary**

The stages of a butterfly's life

Every butterfly has four stages to its life: egg, caterpillar (larva), chrysalis (pupa), and adult. The gradual passage through the four stages is known as metamorphosis.

The cycle begins as the adult female lays her eggs, each one covered by a strong membrane known as chorion. Freshly laid eggs are generally yellow-white, but their color changes and can become quite showy as the chorion dries and becomes solid.

The eggs might be laid singly like the Monarch's, in chains like the Question Mark's, in rows like the Baltimore's, or in clusters like the Tawny Emperor's. There might be only a few of them, or there might be several hundred.

Egg production in some species can be inextricably linked to food availability. Many of the Sulfurs, for example, are not able to lay eggs without having ingested nectar. Females of the Checkerspot species have laid only half of their normal quota when they were not fed.

The shape and texture of butterfly eggs varies from the ribbed vase of the Queen, to the smooth sphere of the Tiger Swallowtail, to the segmented oblong of the Falcate Orangetip. Blues generally lay flat, beehive-shaped eggs, while Whites generally lay tall, thin eggs.

In a depression somewhere on the surface of each egg is the micropyle. In mating, this opening allowed the male's spermatozoa to penetrate the egg. Now it allows the tiny embryo inside the egg to breathe.

The eggs of some species will lie dormant until hatching the following spring. Others will hatch before the approaching winter has arrived. Temperature is the environmental factor that has the most influence over their development.

Most butterfly species are severely limited to one or only a few closely related plant species that can successfully serve as host plants for the caterpillars that will hatch from their eggs. Partly through the co-evolution of host plant and butterfly species, the caterpillars of some species have come to actually need certain chemical constituents that only specific plant species can provide. These specialized chemicals may have originally evolved in the plants as a repellent to most insects, while the caterpillars in turn became so adapted to coping with them that they now actually need them for proper development.

Thus, caterpillars can be monophagous, living off only one plant species; oligophagous, living off a few related plant species; or polyphagous, living off plant species from different families. In some of the monophagous species, the specialization sometimes extends as far as only certain parts of the plant.

The most catholic of the polyphagous species appear to base their host plant selection on a determination of which plants are most succulent and abundant.

Feeding, growth, and energy storage are the only functions of this next phase, the caterpillar that hatches from the eggs. The caterpillar's body is composed of 13 segments, plus a rounded head that sports a pair of antennae. Several pairs of simple eyes, known as ocelli, are found on many species.

But it is the mouth that is the true functional equipment of this chewing machine. A pair of powerful, platelike mandibles or jaws, usually equipped with teeth along their inner edges, protrude between the upper and lower lips.

The lower lip also is the location of the spinnerets, the outlets for the silk glands. With these mechanisms the caterpillar spins the silk or secretes the liquid to secure itself as it enters the chrysalis stage. Only the larvae are equipped with these mechanisms.

The caterpillar propels itself via three pairs of jointed legs, one pair on each of three thoracic segments, and nonjointed prolegs that generally appear in pairs on the third, fourth, fifth, sixth, and tenth segments of the abdomen. The tenth-segment pair is often modified into antennae-like ornaments, an adaptation designed to confuse potential predators.

Internally the caterpillar is quite similar to the adult butterfly, although its glands are much more highly developed. In addition to the silk glands, the caterpillar carries the necessary glands to produce the hormones that regulate its molting and growth. Two antagonistic hormones are responsible for the amazing feat: the molting hormone known as ecdysone and secreted by the prothoracic gland, and the juvenile hormone secreted by the copora allata, located behind the brain.

Some species also have a gland in the thorax that produces an acidic liquid that can be secreted as a defense when necessary.

Moulting to grow

As the caterpillar eats and grows, it must shed (or molt) its nonexpandable skin several times, entering and exiting several stages between molts that are known as instars. The number of molts varies from three to five, according to species, temperature, and food availability. Feeding stops during each molt, as the caterpillar rests for a day or two and replaces its cuticle covering.

When the caterpillar is fully grown, the next molt results in the chrysalis—a nonfeeding, stationary, resting/transforming stage. During this period, the chrysalis nears complete immobility, with the exception of severely limited adjustment and defense motions. The anal and genital openings are sealed. Breathing is accomplished through the spiracles.

In some species such as the Mourning Cloak, the chrysalis hangs by its tail, attached to its host plant by a silken pad known as the cremaster. Inside this shell, nearly all of the larval tissues are broken down and rebuilt into the organs of the adult butterfly. When the full transformation has taken place, the skin of the chrysalis splits open and the butterfly—in the winged form that we tend to visualize in connection with the name—crawls free.

At this point, its wings are frail, shriveled things that are barely opened. The butterfly immediately sets about pumping hemolymph (insect blood) through the veins of the wings, which gradually spread to their full size. After they have stiffened, the insect is ready for flight. There will be no further growth after this final molt, the emergence. This is the final stage of this butterfly's life. Small butterflies do not grow into large butterflies.

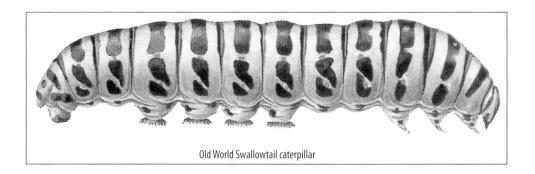

Old World Swallowtail caterpillar

The adult butterfly

The primary task for the insect now is reproduction, and very shortly after it can fly the adult begins its courtship, followed by mating and laying of the eggs. Courtship can include wing stroking between partners, aerial dances, and prenuptial flights. Mating might last several hours, and this is in flight for many species. This adult stage can last from a week to eight months, varying from one species to the next, with most averaging two to three weeks.

The body of the adult butterfly has three segments: head, thorax, and abdomen. It has no inner skeleton but is supported and enveloped by a multilayered exoskeleton. This external integument is of uniform thickness but has less strengthened lines so that movement is possible.

The head features a pair of clubbed antennae, two palpi, two compound eyes, and one long, coiled proboscis. Smell, touch, and orientation are accomplished via the antennae, while the palpi also receive sensations and protect the sensitive proboscis. Each eye is made up of thousands of facets that transmit what is thought to be one integrated, color image to the butterfly's brain.

Butterflies, under experimental conditions, have been found to be able to distinguish between two points separated by only 30 microns, while the minimum possible for humans is 100 microns. A micron is equal to one-millionth of a meter. The butterfly is also able to see ultraviolet light invisible to humans, enabling the insect to differentiate between flowers that appear entirely alike to the human eye.

On the other hand, the butterfly eye is not nearly as well developed as that of the human in terms of seeing at a distance. It has been estimated that the insect's compound eye would need to be more than a meter in diameter to equal the resolution offered by the human eye. The differences reflect the needs of two contrasting lifestyles.

The proboscis is actually the outer lobes of the insect's upper jaws that have been modified into two tubes that extend parallel to one another and are linked to work like a pair of drinking straws. Equipped with alternating rings of membranes and muscles, it can be folded in a spiral under the head or fully extended to drink nectar.

The thorax is made up of three segments. A half dozen legs and the butterfly's four wings are attached to this section of the body.

Each leg of the insect is jointed in five sections: coxa, trochanter, femur, tibia, and tarsus. The clawed tarsi serve as feet and perform a sensing function similar to taste. Their contact with a nectar or similar liquid causes a reflexive uncoiling of the proboscis. Females also use them in scratching and sampling potential host plants for their eggs.

The forelegs of some, like the Brush-footed butterflies, have degenerated into tiny appendages no longer useful in walking.

Wondrous wings

Wings are attached to the thorax by small structures at their bases, to which are connected systems of internal muscles. These muscles are used to move the wings, but they can also be moved by alterations in the thorax shape. The insertion points on the thorax are covered by mobile tegulae.

The wings are composed of double membranes crisscrossed by several tubular veins to hold their structure in place. These veins also transmit insect blood (hemolymph), function as part of the insect's respiration process, and provide ducts for the nervous system.

Hairs and flattened hairs (scales) cover the wing surface. They are held in place in their roof-tile-like arrangement by short stalks inserted into the cuticle.

The brilliant butterfly colors come to the wings either through the pigments in the scales or in the structures of their surfaces. Both the pigment and structural colors are often present at the same spot on the wings, producing a truly spectacular display.

Pigmentation is caused by chemical substances produced through various metabolic processes. For example, urea—a waste product—gives rise to the white, yellow, and orange pigments (pterins) in members of the family Pieridae, a unique trait of these species alone. Melanin, a common pigment, causes the blacks and browns. Others include erythropterin, red; chrysopterin, orange; xanthopterin, yellow; and leucopterin, white.

The Old World Swallowtail

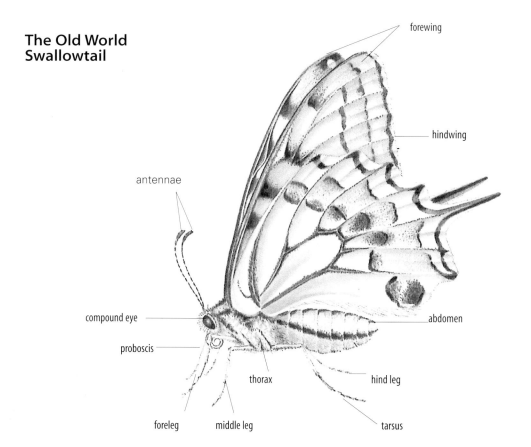

- forewing
- hindwing
- antennae
- compound eye
- proboscis
- thorax
- hind leg
- abdomen
- foreleg
- middle leg
- tarsus

Structural color is a mechanical process, requiring no pigments to produce its generally iridescent colors. The exact process can be accomplished through ridges on the flat surface of the scale, tiny granules in a contrasting medium, or thin films. Blue is always a structural color, as are any metallic effects.

Characteristics

Coloration is one of the characteristics that can vary within a given population for both genetic and nongenetic reasons. Despite common lineage, individuals can vary due to mutations of their genetic makeup. Far from the science fiction image of the word, mutation is a totally natural and surprisingly common occurrence. Whether the mutated variation continues beyond a single generation or not depends on its interaction with the environment. Charles Darwin, the originator of modern evolutionary thought, termed this process natural selection.

In addition, sexual dimorphism, whereby the sexes

The Caligo genus are tropical butterflies of the Brassolidae family who possess huge eyespots on their ventral hindwings.

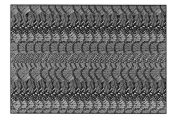

Wing pattern of the Monarch butterfly (Danaus plexippus).

are easily identified by their differences (most notably wing pattern and color) is relatively common in butterflies. There is also a rare condition known as gynandromorphism, in which both male and female characteristics are found in different parts of the same body. This is caused when the sexual chromosomes are separated irregularly during the first divisions of the egg cell.

The same species can also vary according to geography, gradually when the population is distributed continuously without significant physical barriers, or markedly when the various populations are isolated from one another. If the isolation persists over a long period, the populations may also become reproductively isolated. They are then distinct species.

Also on the wings of some males are specialized scent scales, known as androconia. They can be arranged in groups, scattered across the surface of the wing among other scales, or concentrated in patches called stigmata.

The 11 segments of the abdomen carry the insect's sexual and digestive mechanisms, as well as a row of spiracles on each side that allow for the intake of air.

Looking closely

Butterfly experts rely on the genitalia at the rear of the abdomen for exact species identification. This is because there are very limited variations in these organs within species but wide variations between species. Among some groups, notably the skippers, the genitalia are the only reliable method for identification. Such identification generally necessitates dissection and magnification.

Despite this variation, the sex organs generally follow a basic pattern. The male's two testes are connected by canals to the ejaculatory duct, which discharges through the aedeagus.

The female's two ovaries, where the eggs develop, are linked to one common oviduct, which may end in the anal duct or lead to the outside separately. In about 97 percent of all species the female has two genital openings: one for copulation and one for egg laying. Special mechanisms are connected to the female apparatus to gather spermatozoa from the male and release them gradually as the eggs are laid.

Several broods can be produced each year by some species in warmer regions, but those in the mountains or arctic regions might bring only one brood to maturity every two years. While family patterns generally are carried through, many species with more than one brood per year show radical seasonal variation. For example, spring broods in species of the family Pieridae tend to be much paler, with reduced borders and spots, than later broods.

The digestive system begins with the pharynx, equipped with strong muscles to produce the sucking action of the proboscis. The esophagus extends into the insect's body from the pharynx, ending in a crop that accepts and holds the nutritive portion of the butterfly's intake. A digestive tube leads from the terminus of the esophagus to the final outlet for waste matter through the anus.

Like most other living things, butterflies also have nervous, circulatory, and respiratory systems.

The butterfly brain is found in its head, along with another brainlike mass, known as the suprasophagael ganglion, that controls the workings of the mouth. A connected series of ganglia lead from the brain through the length of the abdomen. Lateral nerves connect to this chain to serve all regions of the body.

Unlike vertebrate systems, the butterfly's circulatory system is not physically connected to the respiratory system. A dorsal vessel extends from the abdomen into the thorax, where an aorta is formed. A series of openings connect this primary organ to the rest of the body to circulate the hemolymph (insect blood) through the tissues.

Butterfly respiration is accomplished through a bodywide tracheal system connected to the external environment through stigmas (pores). The system transports oxygen directly to the butterfly's organs without utilizing the blood stream.

The body of the adult butterfly has three segments: head, thorax and abdomen.

When not being used for drinking the butterfly's proboscis can be folded in a spiral under its head.

Predators

In all their life stages, butterflies fall mostly into the prey category, although a few species such as the Harvester are predators as well. The Harvester, the only North American member of a tropical family of carnivorous butterflies, feeds almost exclusively on woolly aphids and their aphid honeydew. But, for the most part, butterflies are prey to a large number of other animals, including other insects, birds, lizards, frogs, toads, and small mammals.

A few species carry a repellent, generally introduced from the host plant on which they feed, but protection usually means concealment or escape. Both of these functions are served in varying degrees by the animal's form and coloration, and almost every manner employed to this end in the animal kingdom is represented somewhere among the butterflies. There are a half dozen primary types:

- Warning coloration incorporates bright, easily seen colors and patterns, with the goal of attracting attention. Species that are inedible because of the poisonous or noxious nature of the plants they eat, employ such coloring to actually advertise this fact to potential predators and to warn them. The Monarch, given its poisonous/noxious ability from the milkweed on which the caterpillar feeds, is the most famous example. Its familiar orange-brown coloring signals its presence from quite a distance, but its slow, meandering flight indicates its lack of concern over that fact.

- The Viceroy is the classic example of mimicry in coloration. Feeding on poplar and willow, the butterfly would be satisfactory food for birds. But it carries the colors and habits of the Monarch and thus gains protection from birds that have learned to avoid anything resembling a Monarch.

- Some species have coloration and shape that give them the appearance of some object that holds no interest for potential predators. The young brown and white caterpillar of the Tiger Swallowtail, for example, is a nearly exact replica of a bird dropping.

- Other species employ coloration and shape to blend into their backgrounds, such as the dull, leafy-colored adult of the Eyed Brown.

- Flash-and-confuse coloration allows species like the American Painted Lady to suddenly expose and hide bright, flashy colors in escape attempts. The butterfly shows the dull coloration of one side of its wings while resting, then flashes gaudy colors in flight, and finally returns suddenly to the dull coloration as it drops. The predator is generally left behind.

- Disruptive coloration, such as the black bands and red-orange or yellow spots of the Eastern Black Swallowtail caterpillar, breaks up the insect's outline to provide protection.

Parasites are an even greater danger than predators, and the chief threats come primarily from viruses and bacteria that remain only poorly understood. Members of two other insect orders, Diptera (flies) and Hymenoptera (wasps, bees, and the like), also do a lot of parasitic damage to some butterfly species.

In general these insects do not kill the butterfly immediately. Instead the female parasite lays her eggs on the butterfly, often in the caterpillar stage, and the developing parasitic larvae feed on their host. Often one of these parasites will emerge from a chrysalis in place of an adult butterfly.

While most parasites attack the caterpillar phase of the butterfly, no stage is completely predator-free.

Black-eared mouse (Peromyscus melanotis). Mice feed at night on live, dying and recently dead butterflies which they find on the forest floor. This is one of the reasons butterflies are at risk when on the ground.

The monarch migration

Fall is a season of change, not only for the leaves on the trees, but for many migrating wildlife species.

It is during this season that millions of Monarch butterflies are migrating to warmer climates for the winter—heading either to the Californian coast or to certain mountains in Mexico.

This annual passage is similar to the type of migration we would expect from birds, whales, and indeed many other mammals. However, unlike mammals, the Monarchs make this return journey only once. The Monarch butterflies know fall is here for the same reason that we do—they feel the coolness in the air. While we can adapt by putting on extra clothing, the situation is much more serious for the butterfly. Temperatures below 55°F make it impossible for them to fly; while temperatures below 40°F actually paralyze them. The Monarchs originated in the tropics and are unable to live for long at temperatures below freezing.

While the temperature is dropping, the nectar supply that feeds the butterflies is also running out. To survive the winter period, the insects start to migrate in late summer, flying with the wind to reach their winter homes.

As many as 100 million Monarch butterflies migrate each year. There are more than 25 winter roosting sites along the Californian coast and about a dozen known sites in the Sierra Madre Oriental Mountains of Mexico. In both regions, butterflies depend upon trees for their survival. The insects gather in pine and eucalyptus trees along the California coast and in ovamel trees in Mexico, and resemble massive clumps of feathery orange-and-black grapes hanging from the trees. Each butterfly hangs with its wings over the butterfly beneath it, creating a shingle effect that buffers the insects from the rain and creates warmth. The weight of the cluster also prevents the butterflies from being blown away.

Butterflies stay in their winter homes until about March, when they begin a quick retreat to their summer homes, at times traveling as fast as 30 mph (48 kmh).

Butterfly watching

Aside from raising butterflies and photographing them, the simple pastime (or for some the passion) of butterfly watching is growing rapidly in popularity. While butterflies have not attracted the millions of fans that birds have won over, there is every indication that someday butterfly watching will be every bit as popular as bird watching.

Tools for the sport are simple. A comprehensive field guide that you are comfortable using is a must. If you can't get the feel of a particular guide and have trouble trying to use it quickly, try another, and another, until you have found the one that suits your method of identification.

Tuck a notebook into your pocket or pack to record all the things you are about to observe. At a minimum, keep track of the species you see, the plants they visit, their behavior, time, and date. Behavior of some species remains only poorly recorded, and amateurs have made important contributions in this area through the comprehensive notes they maintained.

You may even want to borrow the concept of a "life list" from the bird watching fraternity, trying to add as many different species as possible to it over the years. To measure your butterfly accomplishments, remember that geography generally limits the total number of species in even the best locale to less than 100.

A net for temporary capture can help to gently hold a specimen in place while you flip through your field guide at close range. With just a bit of practice, you'll be able to net the insects without doing them any harm.

You might want to add binoculars to your pack. They can be quite handy in observing intimate details of the butterfly's life without having to get too close to it. A pair that focuses quickly and closely is the only type to consider for butterfly watching.

When trying to locate specimens for observation, remember that the greatest diversity of species will be found in open, sun-bathed areas that have abundant flowers.

Butterfly families

The Directory section of this pocket guide has been divided into four butterfly families. It starts with the most colorful of the butterfly families, the Swallowtails (*Papilionidae*), followed by the Whites (*Pieridae*), Brush-footed butterflies (*Nymphalidae*) and finally the Hairstreaks, Coppers, and Blues (*Lycaenidae*).

Papilionidae

Swallowtails are some of the most beautiful types of butterflies. There are around 600 to 700 known species of swallowtails. In North America alone there are about 35 known species of Swallowtail butterflies. The most overriding characteristic of the Swallowtail is the long tail, but of course there are many exceptions. They are usually black, brown, and yellow with red and blue spots. Their average wingspan is 2 to 12 in. (5 to 30.5 cm). Swallowtail are beautiful and amazing butterflies, and it is possible to identify them by looking at their wings. If it is a swallowtail it will usually have "tails" at the bottom of its hindwings. There are more than two dozen species of Swallowtail butterflies in the United States, and most of their caterpillars feed on trees and shrubs. Tiger swallowtails, so called because they are yellow with black stripes, feed on hardwood trees such as cherry and birch. A black and white striped species, appropriately called the Zebra Swallowtail, feeds on pawpaw. Giant swallowtail caterpillars sometimes feed on citrus trees in the South and are called orange dogs. The Black Swallowtail, which is largely black in color, is the "black sheep" of the group and feeds on carrots and parsley.

Pieridae

The Pieridae family of butterflies includes the Whites and Sulfurs, which are easy to identify from their bright colors. The Whites are a large and widespread group which have white and cream colors. They can be found worldwide from Greenland to Patagonia, through the tropics, Neotropics, Asia, Temperate, and Subtropical regions. Adults are small to medium-sized and both sexes have six walking legs. There are 400 to 600 species of Sulfurs, which are generally yellow or white with short, thickly scaled antennae. They are commonly found in open areas and tend to migrate in large numbers. Adults feed on flower nectar and on larval foodplants belonging to the cabbage family.

Florida White (Appias Drusilla) from Pieridae family

Nymphalidae

Nymphalidae is the largest butterfly family, with sizes that vary from large to small, however, most are medium in size. Brush-footed butterflies include groups such as Browns, Milkweeds, Aristocrats, and Snouts. They show a great diversity of color and pattern, but generally brown is the predominant color. One distinct characteristic of this family of butterflies is that only four legs can be seen, and their forelegs are small and hairy, resembling tiny brushes, and are not used for walking. There are at least 150 species of Nymphalidae that can be found in North America, with 47 occurring in Idaho. The butterflies in this

Large Tortoiseshell (Nymphalis Polychloros) from
Nymphalidae family

family vary considerably in their appearance, and are often brightly and/or uniquely marked. The pattern of wing veins of the forewing is unique, and the rigid antennae are tipped with little knobs, called clubs. Interesting traits demonstrated by some members of this family include lengthy migrations, territoriality, and the ability to overwinter as adults. Eggs vary in shape and in their arrangement on the plant. Caterpillars vary considerably in their appearance, but are often hairy or spiny. Pupae have a cremaster from which they are suspended upside down, but have no silk girdle and form no cocoon.

Lycaenidae

This family of butterflies includes three main groups the Hairstreaks, Coppers, and Blues, each of which can be identified by differing external characteristics. Members of this family are generally small, although some of the tropical species can reach 2½ in. (65 mm). The family is known as the Gossamer-Winged butterflies because their wings, like the fabric, generally appear delicate and shimmery. Their wings are covered both by pigmented scales and by light-refracting scales. The male butterfly in this family have reduced forelegs, while those of the female are full-sized. Most of the Hairstreaks have a thin tail extending from the rear of the hindwing. Eggs generally appear round and flattened. Caterpillars generally are small, shaped like slugs and hairy. The caterpillars of many of the species of Blues and Hairstreaks have a dorsal nectary organ which produces a sugary solution which is attractive to ants. The ants feed on the solution and in turn protect the caterpillar from predators (this behavior is referred to as "tending"). Pupae are generally small and round, may have a silk girdle, and are located near or on the ground. Generally no cocoon is formed. Overwintering occurs as either the egg, caterpillar, or pupa.

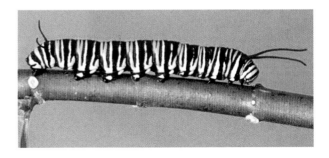

The caterpillar of the Monarch butterfly feeds exclusively on milkweed plants, gaining a noxious taste which protects it from predators.

How to use this guide

Genus:

Battus

Common name:

Blue Swallowtail

Size:

7 to 8.5 cm (2¾ to 3½ in.)

Male or female specimen:

Male

Locality:

North America in open areas

Host plants:

Honeysuckle, milkweed, azalea, lilac,

thistle, phlox, clover, fruit tree blossom

Conservation status:

Status conserved or protected in some

way.

This pocket guide is divided up into four different sections: Papilionidae, Pieridae, Nymphalidae, and Lycaenidae. The heading at the top of the page shows the Latin name and the common name of each butterfly. There is also a fact box giving details of its genus, other common names, the size of its wingspan which is measured from apex to apex, the general type of area or locality where it can be found, a list of plants where the adults can obtain nectar, and finally its conservation status.

Where a common name is known, the European common name is given first, followed by the US common name.

The sizes given in this book are given in imperial and metric and are for the wingspan. The wingspan is the distance between the tips of the outstretched forewings. This is a little larger than twice the forewing length, since it includes the width of the thorax which can be ¼ in. (6 mm) in certain species.

Another point to note is that the butterflies in the color plates are not necessarily to scale. As some of the butterflies are so small, to show them at their true size would mean they would be hardly visible. The majority of the specimens shown in this guide are male, but to identify the butterflies their gender is identified in the fact box.

The conservation status tells you whether a butterfly is in any way conserved or protected.

There is a general description of each butterfly, but as they may vary considerably within the species the author has attempted to cover all possibilities of identification.

Family
Papilionidae

These butterflies are called swallowtails because they have long "tails" on their hindwings which look a bit like the long, pointed tails of swallows. They are generally large and colorful butterflies and include the birdwings of Southeast Asia, which are the largest butterflies in the world. The Swallowtail butterflies are found worldwide except in the Arctic.

Swallowtails have long been a favorite with collectors, and many species are now protected in an effort to save them from extinction.

Allancastria · Cerisyi Cypria

Description

Allancastria (*above*) is a small genus of butterflies which is closely related to the parnassians. This butterfly can be identified by its scalloped hindwing attached to which are small tails. It is a pale yellow in color with distinct black markings. There is only one generation each year. The adult butterfly can be found over alpine meadows where it searches for the *Aristolochia* species, which is the food the caterpillar feeds on.

Genus:
  Allancastria
Common names:
  Eastern Festoon
Size:
  62 mm (2⅜ in.)
Male or female specimen:
  Male
Locality:
  Europe, alpine meadows
Host plants:
  Aristolochia: clematitis, altissima, bodamae, rotunda
Conservation status:
  Not protected

Archon · Apollinus

Description

The female is larger than the male and there is only a single generation each year. They are orange in color with a stronger shade of red on the hindwings. Officially classed as endangered, the False Apollo is most commonly found in Greece and Turkey. Its close relative Archon Apollinaris, or Little False Apollo, is similar in appearance, but much smaller and is usually seen in South Eastern Turkey.

Genus:
  Archon
Common names:
  False Apollo
Size:
  62 mm (2⅜ in.)
Male or female specimen:
  Male
Locality:
  Europe and Africa
Host plants:
  Aristolochia species
Conservation status:
  Protected in Greece

Atrophaneura · Liris

Description

This genus of butterflies is closely related to the *Troides* swallowtails, but tend to be smaller with shorter wings. The males can be either with or without tails, and also have a distinctive dorsal fold from which their scent emanates. They can be found from India to China, through Sulawesi. The *A. liris* swallowtail has long, drawn-out hindwings and a tail. On the underside of the hindwing are five red spots, and these are more pronounced in the female than on the male. There are at least six known subspecies, and at present the species is in no danger of diminishing numbers. It can be found on several of the Indonesian islands.

Genus:
  Atrophaneura
Common names:
  None
Size:
  130 mm (5 in.)
Male or female specimen:
  Male
Locality:
  Indonesian islands
Host plants:
  Mixed forests
Conservation status:
  Not protected

above: Atrophaneura neptunus (Yellow-bodied Club-tail, Yellow Club-tail)

Atrophaneura · Luchti

Description

You can identify this swallowtail butterfly by the bright flash of lemon yellow on its hindwings. The rest of the body is dark and lives typically in the rainforests of eastern Java. As yet its caterpillar foodplants and complete life cycle are not known. It has been classified as rare and is one of the threatened swallowtail butterflies of the world.

Genus:
  Atrophaneura
Common names:
  None
Size:
  140 mm (5½ in.)
Male or female specimen:
  Female
Locality:
  Eastern Java
Host plants:
  Not known
Conservation status:
  Rare and protected

Battus · Philenor

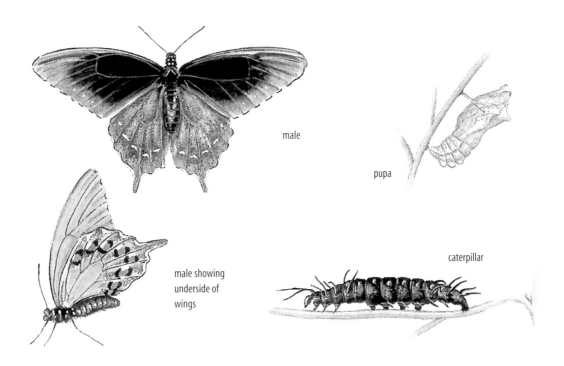

male

pupa

caterpillar

male showing
underside of
wings

Description

This butterfly is also known as the Blue Swallowtail
This butterfly is also known as the Blue Swallowtail
because of its hindwings, which are mostly
shimmering blue above, with black forewings.
Pipevine Swallowtails have become more prolific with
the spread of agricultural areas across the United
States, increasing the supply of the caterpillar"s host
plant. The caterpillar itself takes on the noxious taste
of its host plant, the pipevine, which is an effective
deterrent to most predators. Several other species of
butterfly mimic this butterfly, gaining protection from
its noxious quality.

Genus:
Battus
Common names:
Pipevine Swallowtail
Size:
72 to 92 mm (2¾ to 3½ in.)
Male or female specimen:
Male
Locality:
United States
Host plants:
Pipevines
Conservation status:
Not protected

Battus · Polydamas

male showing
underside of
wings

Description

This butterfly got its other name, the Gold Rim
Swallowtail, from the single band of yellow checks on
the edges of its wings. Red "V"-shaped patterns are on
the underside of the wings, and this is the only tailless
black species of swallowtail in the United States. One
year there may be almost none of this species to be
seen in its normal habitat, while the next year it might
be abundant. The caterpillar, like the *Philenor*, takes on
the taste of its host plant, the pipevine. The chrysalis
varies in color from brown to green.

Genus:
  Battus
Common names:
  Polydamus Swallowtail, Gold Rim
  Swallowtail
Size:
  75 to 102 mm (3 to 4 in.)
Male or female specimen:
  Male
Locality:
  United States
Host plants:
  Pipevines
Conservation status:
  Not protected

Bhutanitis · Thaidina

Description

This is a small genus of butterflies, two of which are very
rare. There is not a lot of information available about
this Swallowtail. The *B. thadina* is easily identified by the
unusual shape of its wings. Especially significant are the
elongated hindwing and its spatula-shaped tail. The
forewing is covered with web-like yellow markings, with
bright red and blue marks on the hindwing. There is not
a lot known about this butterfly, and the species occurs
in China and Tibet. It is quite rare and protected in
certain districts.

Genus:
  Bhutanitis
Common names:
  Three-tailed Bhutan Glory
Size:
  96 mm (3¾ in.)
Male or female specimen:
  Male
Locality:
  China and Tibet
Host plants:
  Not known
Conservation status:
  Protected

Cressida · Cressida

Description

This genus only has one species and they can be found along the north and eastern coastal regions of Australia, including Brisbane. The forewings of the adult butterflies have black veins, two black spots by each forewing costa, and a black area around the base. They are otherwise transparent. The hindwings are black with a white band across each one. They each have a red spot on top, and an arc of red spots underneath. In this way it mimics other Australian Swallowtails. Initially the forewings are white, but the scales are very loose, and soon fall off leaving them transparent. The caterpillar is covered in tubercles, and is mottled with dark brown and white. It feeds on various species of the genus *Aristolochia*. Eggs are yellow, spherical, and ribbed, while the pupa is brown with white markings.

Genus:
  Cressida
Common names:
  None
Size:
  100 mm (4 in.)
Male or female specimen:
  Male
Locality:
  Coastal regions of Australia
Host plants:
  Aristolochia family
Conservation status:
  Not protected

Ellepone · Anactus

Description

This Australian monotypic genus has only recently been described. The Ellepone Anactus, also known as the Dingy Swallowtail or Dainty Swallowtail, is distinctly marked with brown and white patterned wings and a row of red patches bordering the hind wings.

It first evolved on the native citrus plants of the Eastern states but has adapted to the introduced citrus trees.

Genus:
  Elleppone
Common name:
  Dingy Swallowtail
Size:
  60mm (2¾ in)
Male or female specimen:
  Male
Locality:
  Australian region
Host plant:
  Citrus trees
Conservation status:
  not protected

Eurytides · Marcellus

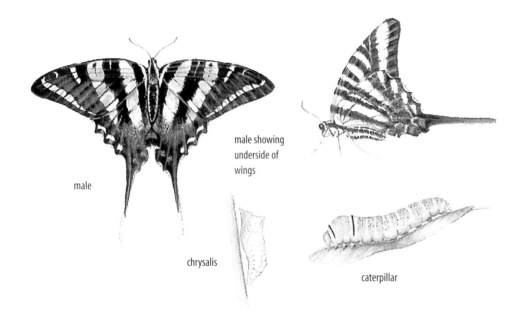

male

male showing underside of wings

chrysalis

caterpillar

Description

The Zebra Swallowtail is a very unique species with black and white banding patterns on all four wings. It is also characterized by its long tails. Fall specimens are generally small with short wings, short tails, and restricted dark and extensive light markings. Later fall and summer specimens are much larger with longer wings, and heavier, darker markings. The majority of Zebra Swallowtails have red spots and red bands of color on the lower wing surfaces. This butterfly can be found from southern New England, west through southern Ontario, Michigan, Minnesota, and Wisconsin, south through central Florida and the Gulf states.

Genus:
Eurytides
Common names:
Zebra Swallowtail
Size:
56 to 90 mm (2¼ to 3½ in.)
Male or female specimen:
Male
Locality:
United States
Host plants:
Pawpaw and related species
Conservation status:
Not protected

Eurytides · Marchandi

Description

Eurytides are a genus of 50 species which are confined to the New World. These butterflies have short antennae which are curved upward and a short, stubby body. Some of the species have long tails and are known as "kite swallowtails." The *marchandi* is a splendid-looking butterfly which has similar characteristics in both the female and male specimens. They have long, slightly curved tails, are predominantly dark brown with strong yellow markings. It inhabits highland rainforest up to around 3,500 ft. (1,067 m), but as yet the foodplants of its caterpillar are unknown.

Genus:
Eurytides
Common names:
None
Size:
100 mm (4 in.)
Male or female specimen:
Male
Locality:
South America
Host plants:
Not known
Conservation status:
Not protected

Graphium · Agamedes

Description

The background colour of this butterfly is a blackish-brown, with broad white bands across its wings. These bands of white are broken by black veins and parts of the forewing are transparent. Both the male and female specimens are similar in appearance. This butterfly can be found in tropical rainforests, and although it is not very common, is not under any protection order. It is generally spotted in the African region, ranging from Ghana to the Central African Republic and south to Zaire. It is generally spotted in the African region, ranging from Ghana to the Central African Republic and south to Zaire.

Genus:
Graphium
Common names:
Glassy Graphium
Size:
65 mm (2½ in.)
Male or female specimen:
Male
Locality:
African region
Host plants:
Not known
Conservation status:
Not protected

Graphium · Antheus

Graphium · Antiphates

Description

This swallowtail has distinctive, long, curved tails and large wings which makes it a strong flier. Both the male and the female are similarly patterned, although the female tends to be a little larger. Males are known to show mud-puddling behavior, which involves sucking up vital salts from the damp earth. Females lay their eggs on members of the *Annonaceae* family, which includes the custard apple. This butterfly is still quite common and not under any threat.

Genus:
Graphium
Common names:
Fivebar Swordtail
Size:
70 mm (2⅝ in.)
Male or female specimen:
Male
Locality:
Asia
Host plants:
Custard Apple (*Annona* species)
Conservation status:
Only threatened in Sri Lanka

Genus:
Graphium
Common names:
Large Striped Swordtail
Size:
100 mm (4 in.)
Male or female specimen:
Male
Locality:
African region
Host plants:
Annonaceae family
Conservation status:
Not protected

Graphium · Aristeus

Graphium · Idaeiodes

Description

These two butterflies get their name from the five long black bars that are predominant on their forewings and lead down toward the dark apex. On the *G. antiphates* the hindwing is scalloped with a long tail which is accentuated by a central black line. The *G. aristeus* is a little smaller and has a pair of beautiful, curved tails.

Description

This is a rare butterfly found in rain forest clearings and along stream edges in the Oriental region. Known specifically to inhabit the Philippine marsh area, it has appeared on two versions of the Philippine sentimo coin. The female has similar markings to the male. .

Genus:
  Graphium
Common names:
  Fivebar Swordtail
Size:
  52 mm (2 in.)
Male or female specimen:
  Male
Locality:
  Asia and Australia
Host plants:
  Custard Apple (*Annona* species)
Conservation status:
  Not protected

Genus:
  Graphium
Common names:
  Not known
Size:
  130mm (5⅛ in)
Male or female specimen:
  Male
Locality:
  Oriental region
Host plants:
  Not known
Conservation status:
  Protected

Graphium · Leonidas

Description

This swallowtail can be found in woodlands, waysides, and gardens, where it sucks nectar from the flowers. The caterpillar feeds on members of the *Annonaceae* family. Both the male and female are similar in coloring, and are adorned with pale green/yellow markings on a darker background.

Graphium Wiskei
(Purple Spotted Swallowtail)
This is one of the most spectacularly coloured of the Swallowtail family, with a beautiful mixture of pink and green. This butterfly frequents the rainforests of New Guinea.

Genus:
  Graphium
Common names:
  Common Graphium,
  Veined Swallowtail
Size:
  89 mm (3½ in.)
Male or female specimen:
  Male
Locality:
  Africa
Host plants:
  Custard Apple (*Annona* species)
Conservation status:
  Not protected

Heraclides · Cresphontes

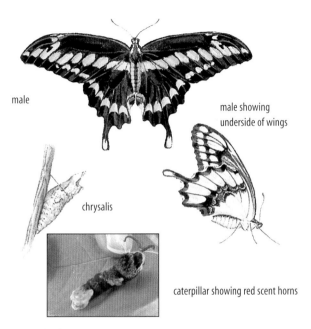

male

male showing underside of wings

chrysalis

caterpillar showing red scent horns

Description

Giant Swallowtails are most common in the southern United States since their larvae are citrus feeders and have been labeled "orange dog" by citrus orchard owners. The caterpillar has the appearance of bird excrement (with the exception of the red scent horns) and also has a very unpleasant smell which acts as a deterrent to would-be predators. On the adult butterfly a band of light yellow patches extends straight across the wings, while a slightly smaller band arches along the rim but converges with the first at the tip of the forewing.

Genus:
  Heraclides
Common names:
  Giant Swallowtail
Size:
  89 to 140 mm (3½ to 5½ in.)
Male or female specimen:
  Male
Locality:
  United States, more common in the South
Host plants:
  Citrus trees
Conservation status:
  Not protected

Iphiclides · Polidarius

Luehdorfia · Japonica

Description

The leaves of the blackthorn are particularly popular amongst caterpillars of the Scarce Swallowtail. There are only two species that belong to this genus and both of them have exceptionally long tails. This butterfly has white wings that are crossed by dark bands. It has a special form of mimicry and could almost be described as flying backward. When it glides through the air showing its false eyes and flowing tails it can be quite convincing. It likes to breed on fruit trees and other *Prunus* species.

These butterflies are a familiar sight among grassy hillsides and flower-filled meadows. The Swallowtail butterfly may live for over half a year as a caterpillar or pupa, but it survives less than a month as a butterfly.

Description

This butterfly appears during April and June depending upon elevation, and is called the 'Goddess of Spring' like *L. puziloi*. The patterning is typical of a swallowtail, with black bars crossing the wing over a pale yellow background. Female lays eggs in a row on *Asarum megacalyx* and occurs in woodland in Japan. It has a modest tail. The hindwing is scalloped and has a distinctive blue eyespot which is surrounded by a curved band of yellow. It has been classified as vulnerable, as it has become quite scarce in certain habitats.

Genus:
  Iphiclides
Common names:
  Scarce Swallowtail
Size:
  90 mm (3½ in.)
Male or female specimen:
  Male
Locality:
  Europe
Host plants:
  Prunus, Pyrus, Malus, Sorbus, Crataegus
Conservation status:
  Not protected

Genus:
  Luehdorfia
Common names:
  Goddess of Spring
Size:
  60 mm (2⅜ in.)
Male or female specimen:
  Male
Locality:
  Asia
Host plants:
  Asarum megacalyx
Conservation status:
  Not protected

Ornithoptera · Aesacus

Description

Very little is known about this butterfly and its only known location is on Obi Island in the Moluccas, Indonesia. The male and female are quite different in appearance. *O. aesacus* is the least known of the three species of the Ornithoptera genus—*aesacus, priamus,* and *croesus*. The male has iridescent turquoise/green wings and a thick black bar on its forewings. The female, however, is brown with white spots and yellow/gray forewings.

Description

The butterfly on the left is a birdwing which is being farmed in the Bismarck Archipelago, on Bougainville, and also can be found in the Solomon Islands. The middle part of its forewings is a wonderful rich, velvety brown, which is surrounded by an equally rich velvet-blue, while the contrasting abdomen is bright yellow.

Genus:
  Ornithoptera
Common names:
  None
Size:
  60 mm (2⅜ in.)
Male or female specimen:
  Male and female
Locality:
  Obi Island, Indonesia
Host plants:
  Not known
Conservation status:
  Protected

Genus:
  Ornithoptera
Common names:
  D'Urville's Birdwing
Size:
  185 mm (7¼ in.)
Male or female specimen:
  Male
Locality:
  New Ireland, Bougainville, Solomon Islands
Host plants:
  Not known
Conservation status:
  Protected

Pachliopta · Polydorus Utuanensis

Description

This genus of butterflies is sometimes combined with *Atrophaneura*. There are more than a dozen species within this genus and they can be found in India and Australia. These butterflies are inclined to breed on the poisonous plants of the *Aristolochia* family, and they store the poisons within their systems to act as their own defense against predators. Some of the species also carry red marks on their bodies to act as an additional warning.

In general, the females are larger than the male, but both sexes are dark in coloring with lighter areas prominent on the surface of their wings. Occasionally they show a series of red spots on the hindwing and also on the underside and tip of the body. The species itself is not under threat, and the smallest specimens have been found in Queensland, Australia.

Genus:
Pachliopta
Common names:
Red-bodied Swallowtail
Size:
80 mm (3⅛ in.)
Male or female specimen:
Male
Locality:
Asia and Australia
Host plants:
Aristolochia family (poisonous members)
Conservation status:
Not protected

Papilio · Aegeus Ormenus

Description

This is a large butterfly commonly found in Brisbane, Australia. The male is black with white or cream crescents and a red spot on each wing. The underneath of the male"s hindwings have less white and more red patches with small blue crescents. The female is similar, but browner, with a white patch on the forewings, showing brown veins. Orchard butterflies in flight are slow and erratic. When settled, their wings are held open widely, and they feed on flowers with their wings vibrating. It takes about one week for an egg to hatch. The newly emerged larva will eat the egg shell as their first meal. The first and second instars larva closely resemble a fresh bird dropping. The larva feed singly on foodplants. They usually feed during the day and rest by night on the upper side of leaves.

above: Papilio Astyalus (Astyalus Swallowtail)
This Swallowtail can be found from Central America into the southern United States, and is found in areas that are forested with tropical hardwoods. Like many other Papilio, the caterpillars like to breed on citrus. On the male butterfly there is an extremely wide band of yellow which crosses the wings. On the edges of the hindwings are six yellow chevron, or V-shaped, marks. The female of the species is very dark in colour and can be with or without a tail.

Genus:
Papilio
Common names:
Orchard Swallowtail, Large Citrus Butterfly
Size:
90 mm (3½ in.)
Male or female specimen:
Male
Locality:
Australia and New Guinea
Host plants:
Citrus trees
Conservation status:
Not protected

Papilio · Demodocus

Papilio · Glaucus

female

male

caterpillar

chrysalis

Description

This common butterfly is found in open woodland, forests and citrus groves and can be considered a pest, although this is a particularly beautiful specimen. The forewings are black and at the margin are two chains of yellow spots. The hind wings sport two large eyes; one black and blue and the other black, blue and red. The underside of this butterfly is almost identical to the upperside, but for a series of yellow lines near the body. It was first described in 1798. There is virtually no difference between the male and female Papilio Demodocus..

Description

The Tiger Swallowtail is thought of as the American insect, in much the same way as the Bald Eagle is thought of as the American bird. It was the first American insect pictured in Europe; a drawing was sent to England from Sir Walter Raleighs" third expedition to Virginia.

Genus:
   Papilio
Common names:
   Citrus Butterfy, African Lime Butterfly, Christmas Butterfly, Orange Dog
Size:
   110mm (4 ⅜ in)
Male or female specimen:
   Male
Locality:
   African region
Host plants:
   Citrus plants
Conservation status:
   Not protected

Genus:
   Papilio
Common names:
   Tiger Swallowtail
Size:
   76 to 140 mm (3 to 5½ in.)
Male or female specimen:
   Male and female
Locality:
   Canada and the United States
Host plants:
   Many trees and shrubs such as willows, birches, cherries, and poplars
Conservation status:
   Not protected

Papilio · Glaucus

DESCRIPTION

The Eastern Tiger Swallowtail ranges from Alaska and the Hudsonian zone of Canada to the southern United States, east of the Rocky Mountains. This species occurs in nearly every area where deciduous woods are present, including towns and cities. It is most numerous along streams and rivers, and in wooded swamps.

male showing
underside of wings

The forewing spans 3 to 5½ in. (76 to 140 mm). The males are yellow, with black tiger stripes, and a large black border surrounds the edges of the wings. In Georgia, the coloring has more of an orange hint. Females are dimorphic, and while some have the same color pattern as the males, others are completely black. A variety of patterns between completely black, and yellow with black stripes can be seen in female swallowtails. These two extremes of coloring in the female are thought to coexist because they both have equally beneficial effects—the tiger striping distracts the predators, while the dark coloring imitates the unpalatable Blue Swallowtail. They reach maturity in the spring, and many generations are produced each year and the last mature butterflies remain into mid-fall.

As with most butterflies, Eastern Tiger Swallowtails tend to be solitary. The males "patrol" for a mate, flying from place to place actively searching for females. "Patrolling" male Tiger Swallowtails can recognize areas of high moisture absorption by the sodium ion concentration of the area. It is believed that the moisture found by these males helps cool them by initiating an active-transport pump. Both male and female Tiger Swallowtails are known to be high fliers. Groups of up to 50 butterflies have been spotted in Maryland flying 54 yards (50 m) high, around the tops of tulip trees.

The larvae are polyphagous, meaning they feed externally on the leaves of various woody plants. Foodplants include a variety of poplars, mountain ash, birch, cherry, tulip tree, ash, basswood, apple, maple, willow, magnolia, and occasionally sassafras. The Eastern Tiger Swallowtails are not yet threatened by human impact on their ecosystem.

Papilio · Indra

male

male showing
underside of wings

Description

The abdomen of the Short-tailed Black Swallowtail is
all black, or black with a yellow dash on the side of the
rear. Wings are mostly black with pale yellow
markings, while the tails are very short on most
subspecies. Males tend to watch from rocky areas
below tops of hills or mesas for receptive females.
Females lay eggs singly on top of host plant leaves or
on flowers. Caterpillars feed on the edges of the leaves
and hide at the base of plants. The chrysalis is broader
than those of other swallowtails, and the winter
months are spent in the chrysalis stage. These
butterflies only take one flight, with occasional late-
flying individuals of desert populations during March
to August.

Several subspecies occur entirely or primarily on
Federal lands. These include *kaibabensis* (Grand
Canyon National Park), *minori* (Colorado National
Monument and B.L.M.), *panamintensis* (Death Valley
National Monument), and *martini* (Mojave Desert
National Preserve).

caterpillar

Genus:
Papilio
Common names:
Short-tailed Black Swallowtail,
Mountain Swallowtail
Size:
52 to 90 mm (2 to 3½ in.)
Male or female specimen:
Male
Locality:
Southern California, Nevada, Arizona,
New Mexico north to South Dakota,
west to Washington
Host plants:
Aromatic herbs of the parsley family
(*Apiaceae*)
Conservation status:
Not protected

Papilio • Machaon

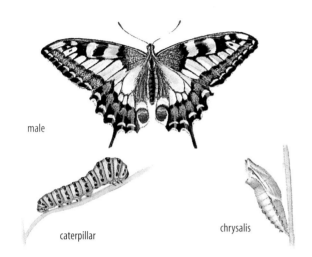

male

caterpillar

chrysalis

Description

The Old World Swallowtail has a broad band of pale yellow spots that cover most of the wings both above and below. Much of the black on the wings is clouded over in yellow or pale blue. The eyespots on the hindwing are red, but have no pupils. This butterfly appears almost completely yellow from underneath. This is the only swallowtail that extends throughout the entire northern extremes of the Northern Hemisphere. It can be found in Europe, North Africa, in the moderate zones of Asia into Japan, and in North America. It is very rarely seen in England. They like open, grassy landscapes, and also quiet areas near water. This butterfly flies in one brood in late June to July. The larvae develop on sagebrush, parsley, and carrot.

female showing underside of wings

Genus:
  Papilio
Common names:
  Old World Swallowtail, Dove Tail Swallowtail
Size:
  65 to 75 mm (2½ to 3 in.)
Male or female specimen:
  Male and female
Locality:
  Europe, North Africa, in the moderate zones of Asia, Japan, North America
Host plants:
  Carrot, parsley, and sagebrush
Conservation status:
  Not protected

Papilio • Memnon

Description

This butterfly is unusual for its great variety of female forms, both tailed or tailless, and for mimicking a number of other species which are unpalatable to birds. It is a widely distributed and variable Swallowtail with at least 13 recorded subspecies. *P. memnon* is a Swallowtail butterfly living in the Malay Archipelago and Indonesia. The males of the species are generally black and never have tails. In the female the forewings are usually pale brown beneath the heavily marked veined areas. The base of each wing is very dark. The butterfly breeds on citrus and can be seen visiting flowers along lowland rainforest areas.

Genus:
  Papilio
Common names:
  Great Mormon
Size:
  120 mm (6 in.)
Male or female specimen:
  Male
Locality:
  Malay, Indonesia and Australia
Host plants:
  Citrus trees
Conservation status:
  Not protected

Papilio · Polyxenes

male

female

male showing
underside of wings

chrysalis

caterpillar

Description

The upper surface of the wings is mainly black, and on the inner edge of the hindwing is a black spot centered in a larger orange spot. The male has yellow bands near the edge of his wings, while the female has a row of yellow spots. The female hindwing has an iridescent blue band. Males perch and patrol for receptive females. Females lay eggs singly on leaves and flowers of the host plant, which are then eaten by hatching larvae, which hibernate as a chrysalis. The adult butterfly feeds off nectar from flowers including red clover, milkweed, and thistles. They can be found in a variety of open areas, including fields, suburbs, marshes, deserts, and roadsides.

They have one to two flights from April to October in northern regions, and three flights in southern regions.

Genus:
Papilio
Common names:
Eastern Black Swallowtail
Size:
120 mm (2¾ to 3½ in.)
Male or female specimen:
Male and female
Locality:
United States
Host plants:
Carrot, celery, dill, parsley family and sometimes citrus family
Conservation status:
Not protected

Papilio • Rumanzovia

Description

The male and female in this genus are totally different and although it is called the Scarlet Mormon the male is mostly very dark with a pale blue dusting on its hindwings. The scarlet is prominent on the female, where it can be seen on both the hind- and forewings. Both sexes have rounded forewings and can be found in the Philippines and Indonesia.

Papilio Ulysses (Ulysses Butterfly, Blue Mountain Swallowtail, Mountain Blue, Blue Emperor). The P. ulysses is one of Australia's most beautiful butterflies, but unfortunately it also makes it very popular with collectors. The male is the brightest with iridescent blue-green contrasting its black background colour. The female is not quite so bright, but both sexes have black tails and irregularly scalloped hindwings. The male of the species are always curious of anything that is coloured blue, and for this reason it is easy to entice them closer for observational purposes. Because of their popularity with collectors this species is protected in Queensland.

Genus:
  Papilio
Common names:
  Scarlet Mormon
Size:
  140 mm (5½ in.)
Male or female specimen:
  Female
Locality:
  Philippines and Indonesia
Host plants:
  Rutaceae
Conservation status:
  Protected in Queensland

Papilio · Troilus

Description

The upper surface of the forewing on this swallowtail is mostly black with ivory spots along the margin, while the upper surface of the hindwing has orange spots on the edge. The underside of the hindwing has pale green marginal spots. Males patrol in woods, roads, and woodland edges to find receptive females. Females lay single eggs on the underside of host plant leaves. Caterpillars live in shelters of folded-over leaves and come out to feed at night. There are two generations per year from April to October, but in Florida, there are several generations between March to December. The adult butterfly feeds on nectar from Japanese honeysuckle, jewelweed, thistles, milkweed, azalea, dogbane, lantana, mimosa, and sweet pepperbush. They favor deciduous woodlands, fields, roadsides, yards, pine barrens, wooded swamps, and parks.

Genus:
  Papilio
Common names:
  Spicebush Swallowtail, Green-clouded Swallowtail
Size:
  126 mm (4⅞ in.)
Male or female specimen:
  Male
Locality:
  United States, Canada, and Cuba
Host plants:
  Spicebush (*Lindera benzoin*), sassafras trees (*Sassafras albidum*); occasionally prickly ash (*Zanthoxylum americanum*), tulip tree (*Liriodendron tulipifera*), sweetbay (*Magnolia virginiana*), camphor (*Cinnamomum camphora*) and redbay (*Persea borbonia*).
Conservation status:
  Not protected

Papilio · Weymeri

Description

This is a rare butterfly which is endemic to two islands in Papua New Guinea. This species lives in the virgin rainforest area, and also some scrub areas, and is known to breed on a rutaceous plant called *Micromelum*. Both sexes are tailless but differ in appearance. The male has a band of large cream markings on its dark forewing and a slightly scalloped hindwing. The female is predominantly brown with white markings on the forewing, and a band of blue and yellow markings on the hindwing. It is classified as rare and is under a protection order..

Genus:
  Papilio
Common names:
  None
Size:
  150 mm (6 in.)
Male or female specimen:
  Male
Locality:
  Papua New Guinea
Host plants:
  Micromelum
Conservation status:
  Protected

Papilio · Zelicaon

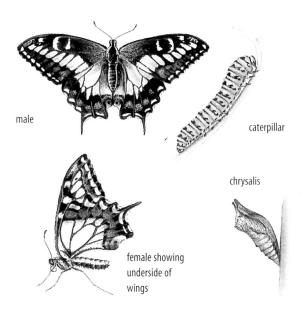

male

caterpillar

chrysalis

female showing underside of wings

Description

This is the most common swallowtail west of the Rocky Mountains. The Male Anise Swallowtail is attracted to elevated areas such as hilltops, and particularly during his courtship period. It is also known to frequently visit mud puddles. A band of bright yellow spots with straight edges extends across the midwings. There are eyespots on the corner of the hindwing closest to the body, and these are red with large, black, centered pupils. The adult butterfly favors the nectar of mints, zinnia, butterfly bush, and penstemon. The caterpillar likes to eat both the leaves and flowers of its host plant.

During the late 1960s, the population of these butterflies appears to have undergone reduction, this is possibly due to the rapid disappearance of its natural foodplant habitat.

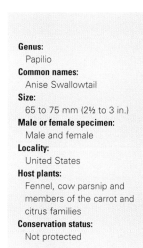

Genus:
  Papilio
Common names:
  Anise Swallowtail
Size:
  65 to 75 mm (2½ to 3 in.)
Male or female specimen:
  Male and female
Locality:
  United States
Host plants:
  Fennel, cow parsnip and members of the carrot and citrus families
Conservation status:
  Not protected

Parides · Ascanius

Description

This beautiful butterfly is commonly called the "Butterfly of the Beach." It is restricted to a very small portion of costal swamp habitat in Rio De Janeiro, Brazil where its host plant, *Aristolochia macroura*, grows. However, the conversion of beachfront habitat into resorts, hotels, and developed areas, together with the draining of vital coastal wetlands have driven this species to near extinction. One colony still exists in the Poço das Antas Reserve and protection of this area may ensure its survival. Both sexes are similar in this genus, with dark forewings which are broken by a large white flash. The flash continues onto the tailed hindwings, which also have a suffusion of pink.

Genus:
  Parides
Common names:
  Ascanius Swallowtail, Fluminense
  Swallowtail
Size:
  68 mm (2⅝ in.)
Male or female specimen:
  Female
Locality:
  South America
Host plants:
  Aristolochia species
Conservation status:
  Protected

Parides · Photinus

Description

This swallowtail is common from northwest Mexico south to Costa Rica. It is also present in eastern Mexico but absent from the drier interior. It is a relatively common genus and is not threatened. It can be seen regularly in lowland and highland rainforests. This very attractive butterfly has just a mere suggestion of two unequal-length tails. The males have a striking blue flourescence to the hindwings, black wings, and two rows of red markings, the inner ones of which are spots and the outer chevrons, that appear on the hindwings. This genus breeds on plants of the *Aristolochia* species.

Genus:
  Parides
Common names:
  Pink-spotted Cattleheart
Size:
  95 mm (3¾ in.)
Male or female specimen:
  Male
Locality:
  Mexico to Costa Rica
Host plants:
  Aristolochia species
Conservation status:
  Not protected

Parnassius · Apollo

Description

The Apollo butterfly is found in all the high mountains of Europe as well as on plains (preferring dry pine and mixed forests). Their flight period is from June to August. Pupation of the larvae takes place in a loose cocoon in the litter or under stones. Being very local and particular in its ecological requirements, this butterfly is very susceptible to changes in its environment and in some cases it has been extinguished. The species is included as endangered in the *International Red Data Book*. It is rather a clumsy flier with white wings which are covered with variable black spots, and red spots on the hindwing. One peculiarity of the female is that it has a special cap which covers the rear of the abdomen after mating, to stop any further copulation.

Genus:
  Parnassius
Common names:
  Apollo
Size:
  80 mm (3⅛ in.)
Male or female specimen:
  Male
Locality:
  The whole of Europe, Tian-Shan and Siberia to Yakutia; also from the N. Urals to Transcaucasia, Asia Minor and the Middle East; Mongolia
Host plants:
  Sedum telephium, S. album, S. rupestre, S. rosea, Hylotelephium caucasicum, Sempervivum, Rhodiola rosea
Conservation status:
  Protected

Parnassius · Clodius

Description

The American Apollo has waxy white wings with three dark gray bars on the forewing. The front wing has no red spots, while the upper surface of the hindwing has two. The female of the species usually has a red anal bar. Mated females have a large, white keeled pouch (*sphragis*) at the end of their abdomen. Males patrol habitat to find females, and after mating they attach a pouch to the female to prevent multiple matings. Females lay single eggs scattered on the host plant. Caterpillars feed at night at the base of the host plant and pupate in a loose silk cocoon above ground. They favor open woods, alpine areas, meadows, and rock outcrops. Twelve subspecies are in existence, including a dark form of which occurs in Alaska. Drought, logging, and damming waterways are thought to be causing problems to populations of this butterfly.

Genus:
  Parnassius
Common names:
  American Apollo, Clodius Parnassian
Size:
  64 mm (2½ in.)
Male or female specimen:
  Male
Locality:
  Western Canada and western United States
Host plants:
  Bleeding heart family (*Fumariaceae*) including *Dicentra uniflora, D. formosa* and *D. pauciflora*
Conservation status:
  Subspecies *strohbeeni* from California's Santa Cruz Mountains is extinct, and quite rare in other parts of its range

Pterourus · Eurymedon

male

male showing underside

Description

Pale Tiger Swallowtails are usually the first to emerge in spring, struggling out of their chrysalis as early as late May. Adults have wings the color of antique ivory with broad tiger stripes running from the front to the back. Borders of the hindwing are marked in orange, pale blue, and off-white. Even the caterpillar is quite pale, its green toned down to the soft shade of new willow leaves. The chrysalis looks like tree bark with its brown and black markings.

Less numerous than other Tiger Swallowtails, the Pale Tiger Swallowtail occurs widely throughout the West. It takes nectar from mints, thistles, and buckeyes. Males settle more often on damp earth, sometimes in great congregations. They prefer mountainous or hilly country with broadleaf scrub or chaparral, dry slopes, canyons, and roads. They have one brood in late spring-midsummer, varying with latitude and altitude. This butterfly is similar in appearance to the Western Tiger Swallowtail, which is more yellow in color and has paler veins.

Genus:
Pterourus
Common names:
Pale Tiger Swallowtail
Size:
75 to 95 mm (3 to 3¾ in.)
Male or female specimen:
Male
Locality:
United States
Host plants:
Ashes, cherries, laurels, willows
Conservation status:
Not protected

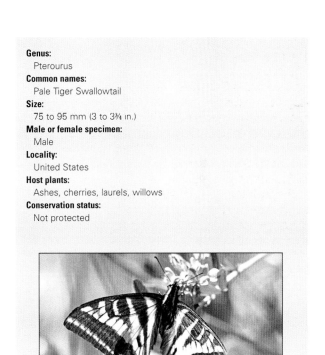

Pterourus · Multicaudatus

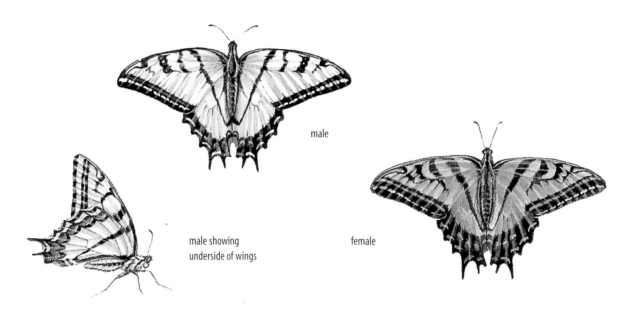

male

male showing
underside of wings

female

Description

This butterfly may reach a size over 5 in. (125 mm) and, as the name implies, it has two tails on each wing. Look closely at the lower edge of each wing to see two longer tails to the outside and two medium tails to the inside. This is the largest genus of the western Tiger Swallowtails and its habitat is widespread, but normally near moisture—canyons, watersides, trails, roadsides, parks and gardens, sagelands and mesas with creeks. It ranges from British Columbia south to Baja California, east through the Rockies to Black Hills, and High Plains of Colorado and New Mexico, but is rare east of the Rockies. The black tiger stripes on the wings of the Two-tailed Tiger Swallowtail are very narrow and short, and extend over bright yellow wings. The caterpillar transforms from bright green to red-brown before pupating.

Genus:
Pterourus
Common names:
Two-tailed Tiger Swallowtail
Size:
85 to 130 mm (3¼ to 5 in.)
Male or female specimen:
Male
Locality:
British Columbia and Montana south to New Mexico and Baja California; and in Cascades, Sierra Nevada, Coast Ranges and Rockies. Absent from drier, hotter parts of basins and deserts
Host plants:
Members of the buckthorn and alder families
Conservation status:
Not protected

Pterourus · Palamedes

male showing

male

caterpillar

chrysalis

Description

Palamedes is usually the most common Swallowtail you"ll see in the coastal plain and usually can be found wherever its host plants are in abundance. They favor wet woods near rivers and broadleaf evergreen swamp forests. When seen, the yellow stripe on the underside makes this butterfly easy to identify. The upper surface of hind- and forewings have postmedian yellow bands, while the tails are filled with yellow. The lower surface of the hindwing has a thin yellow basal stripe and postmedian band of yellow-orange crescents. The adults feed on nectar from flowers of sweet pepperbush, thistles, blue flag, and azalea. They can be found along the Atlantic coast from southern New Jersey to Florida; west and south along the Gulf Coast to central Mexico. The Palamedes Swallowtail spends the winter months in both the caterpillar and the chrysalis forms. It has one to three broods from February through to December.

Genus:
Pterourus
Common names:
Palamedes Swallowtail, Laurel Swallowtail
Size:
75 to 140 mm (3 to 5½ in.)
Male or female specimen:
Male
Locality:
Along Atlantic coast from southern New Jersey (rare) to Florida; west and south along Gulf Coast to central Mexico
Host plants:
Redbay (*Persea borbonia*) and Swampbay (*P. palustris*), aromatic evergreen trees in the laurel family
Conservation status:
Not protected

Pterourus · Rutulus

male

male showing
underside of wings

Description

This is the commonest Swallowtail observed in the
West and a person can attract these butterflies to a
garden by planting zinnias, milkweeds, thistles,
penstemons, and other flowers. It prefers woodlands
near rivers and streams, wooded suburbs, canyons,
parks, roadsides, and oases. The hindwings have tails at
their lower tips that resemble the long tail feathers of
a swallow; hence, their common name swallowtail.
Also on the hindwing, there are narrow yellow spots
along the wing"s margin and orange tint on two spots
near the end of the inner margin of the wing. Blue
spots are found around the outer margin of the
hindwing. The upper side of the hindwing may have a
yellow spot on the outer margin. On the forewing,
yellow spots form a continuous band along the outer
margin of the wing. These yellow spots are bordered
in black. Males patrol canyons or hilltops for receptive
females. Swallowtail females may lay up to four
batches of eggs in a season and up to 100 eggs in
total. The length of time that it takes for the larvae to
emerge from the egg depends upon the weather, but
generally, in summer, it takes four days. The larvae
molt five times—called instars—before they pupate.
After each molt, the caterpillar eats the old skin which
is rich in nutrients.

Genus:
Pterourus
Common names:
Western Tiger Swallowtail
Size:
72 to 102 mm (2¾ to 4 in.)
Male or female specimen:
Male
Locality:
Western North America from British
Columbia south to southern New
Mexico and Baja California; east to
western South Dakota and southeast
Colorado
Host plants:
Leaves of cottonwood and aspen
(*Populus*), willows (*Salix*), wild cherry
(*Prunus*) and ash (*Fraxinus*)
Conservation status:
Not protected

Troides · Haliphron Socrates

Description

Members of this genus range from Southeast Asia in the Oriental Region through part of the Australian Region. It is a large family of Birdwing butterflies and they are characterized by having bright yellow on the hindwings and dark forewings. The male of the *T. haliphron socrates* is jet black with a curved, bright yellow mark in the middle of the hindwing. The female is much larger and is dull brown in color with just a touch of lighter scales, although the hindwing still shows the yellow markings. This butterfly is generally found on the Indonesian islands, and although it is much sought after by collectors it is not thought to be threatened.

Genus:
   Troides
Common names:
   None
Size:
   140 mm (5½ in.)
Male or female specimen:
   Male
Locality:
   Southeast Asia in the Oriental Region
   through part of the Australian Region
Host plants:
   Not identified
Conservation status:
   Not protected

Troides · Helena Cerberus

Description

This spectacular "birdwing" is essentially a jungle species but is drawn to cultivated areas where its foodplant, *Aristolochia tagala,* can be found. Both the male and female share the same black and yellow coloring, which acts as a warning pattern to predators that it is distasteful. This species is highly sought after by collectors and is a protected species in Malaysia and Singapore.

In Singapore, the Common Birdwing can be found at the Botanical Gardens and the Singapore Zoo, where the foodplant can still be found. The female, which is the larger of the two sexes, has a series of black spots on the hindwing.

Genus:
   Troides
Common names:
   Common Birdwing
Size:
   180 mm (7 in.)
Male or female specimen:
   Male
Locality:
   North India to Hainan and Hongkong,
   through Sundaland to Sulawesi
Host plants:
   Aristolochia tagala
Conservation status:
   Protected in Malaysia and Singapore

Zerynthia · Polyxena

Description

This is a genus of rather lazy butterflies which have small wings. They have very complex color markings on their wings and rather hairy bodies. The overall pattern is reversed on the underside of their wings. They breed on poisonous members of the *Aristolochiaceae*, which gives them a nasty taste and wards off would-be predators. The Southern Festoon is from southern Europe and is relatively small, but conspicuously colored with a red warning color which also deters predators. There is also a very similar species, the Spanish Festoon which has more red spots on its wings. They have one brood from March to May. They prefer meadows, near water, where its host plant is abundant.

Genus:
Zerynthia
Common names:
Southern Festoon
Size:
52 mm (2 in.)
Male or female specimen:
Male
Locality:
Southern Europe
Host plants:
Aristolochia species
Conservation status:
Not protected

Zerynthia · Rumina

left: The Spanish Festoon is very similar to the Southern Festoon but there are more red spots and also small transparent spots on the forewings. A widespread species in Spain, they frequent most habitats and are to be seen in relatively low densities nearly everywhere you go.

Description

This butterfly is mostly found in Spain frequenting habitats from montane meadows to rocky slopes. It can be distinguished from its close relative the Eastern Festoon or Zerynthia Cerisy by the propensity of black on its forewing. The male Zerynthia Rumina has a slightly more creamy in coloring and less red markings.

Genus:
Zerynthia Rumina
Common names:
Spanish Festoon
Size:
45mm (1⅞ in)
Male or female specimen:
Female
Locality:
Eurasian region
Host plants:
Birthworts
Conservation status:
Not protected

Family
Pieridae

The Pieridae (often referred to as the Whites and Yellows) also include the Sulfurs or Sulphurs. They do not have any tails and are named after their coloring which is generally white, yellow, or orange. They can be quite prolific around water sources in tropical climates and many, like the Large and Small White, are considered to be pests. Adults tend to be small to medium-sized, and both sexes have six walking legs and distinctly bifid claws. The adults feed on flower nectar and males like to visit wet soil.

Anteos · Maerula

Anteos · Menippe

Description

These bright yellow butterflies are often the first to be seen in spring. The male Brimstone has sulfur-yellow forewings and hindwings with an orange central spot. The female's fore- and hindwings are a delicate yellow or pale green also with a central orange spot. Both sexes have greenish veined underwings. The caterpillars are bluish-green with a pale line down each side, and the pupa resembles a curled leaf. These butterflies can be found in both woodland and gardens, sipping nectar from teasel, knapweed, and buddleia.

Description

This sulfur is a native of Costa Rica and Ecuador and has curved wings with large orange tips and pointed tails. The females lack these orange tips but still have the overall yellow-lemon background color. This is a migrant species and, like other members of the genus, is very active in open sunny areas, particularly beside water. The males often congregate in quite large numbers and participate in mud-puddling.

Genus:
Anteos
Common names:
Yellow Brimstone, Yellow-angled Sulphur
Size:
89 mm (3½ in.)
Male or female specimen:
Male
Locality:
Europe and North Africa
Host plants:
Buckthorn and alder buckthorn
Conservation status:
Protected in Northern Ireland

Genus:
Anthocharis
Common names:
Mammoth Sulphur
Size:
68 mm (2⅝ in.)
Male or female specimen:
Male
Locality:
Central and South America
Host plants:
Cassia species
Conservation status:
Not protected

Anthocharis · Belia

Description

This is a fairly widespread species in Spain in the spring, and can be found along waysides, the edges of woodlands, and in fields full of flowers. The male of the species has a bright yellow background with bright orange tips. The underside of the hindwing is suffused with bold green and yellow marks. The female lacks the bright yellow background coloring of the male. There is a single generation each year and the butterfly breeds on various mustards of the *Cruciferae* family.

Genus:
   Anthocharis
Common names:
   Moroccan Orange Tip
Size:
   40 mm (1½ in.)
Male or female specimen:
   Male
Locality:
   Europe and North America
Host plants:
   Biscutella species including Buckler mustard
Conservation status:
   Not protected

Anthocharis · Lanceolata

Description

This butterfly can be found flying around rocky canyons or forest openings. The males patrol the valleys or draws looking for females. They lay their eggs singly on host plant flowers and leaves, and the caterpillars prefer to feed on the flowers and fruit. The forewing of the *A. lanceolata* is slightly pointed and the outer margin is concave. The top and bottom of the forewing is white with a black cell spot and black margin at the tip. The underside of the hindwing has dark veins, dense gray marbling, and a white blotch underneath the costal margin. There is one single flight each year from March to June.

Genus:
   Anthocharis
Common names:
   California White Tip, Grey Marble
Size:
   44 mm (1¾ in.)
Male or female specimen:
   Male
Locality:
   Southwest Oregon south to northern Baja California, western edge of Nevada
Host plants:
   Rock cress (*Arabis* species) and other mustard family (*Brassicaceae*) plants
Conservation status:
   Not protected but threatened throughout its range

Anthocharis · Midea

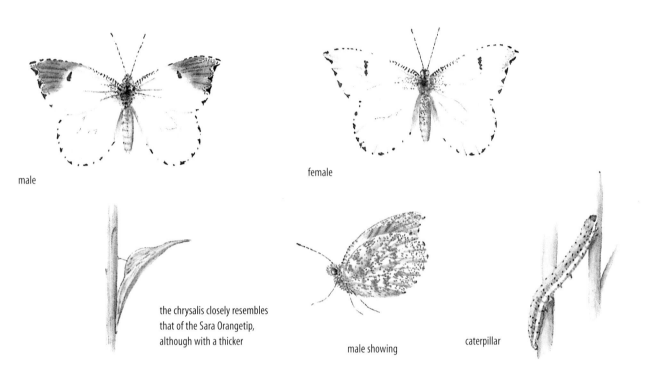

male

female

the chrysalis closely resembles
that of the Sara Orangetip,
although with a thicker

male showing

caterpillar

Description

The Falcate Orangetip is more of a southern species that occasionally strays north. It is a small, white butterfly, with a small black dot in the upper wings and very small black dots at the margins of the wings. The male is very noticeable with orange-tipped forewings. The underwings of both the sexes are similar with a very fine greenish marbling. This butterfly is an inhabitant of mixed and deciduous woodlands, and development could cause a drop in population.

Genus:
Anthocharis
Common names:
Falcate Orangetip
Size:
32 to 40 mm (1¼ to 1½ in.)
Male or female specimen:
Male and female
Locality:
Europe and South America
Host plants:
Mustards
Conservation status:
Not protected

Anthocharis · Sara

male showing underside of wings

Description

This versatile butterfly is very successful in using a wide range of western habitats, from mountain slopes to streams. The upperside of the male forewing has large, orange-red tips framed in black. The tip on the female is smaller, with a dark border and white wedges. The underside of the hindwing is scattered with a dark green marbling. Late spring butterflies are usually larger with less black and have yellow-green marbling. The adults feed on flower nectar, including that of the host mustards, thistles, fiddleneck, and brodiaeas. There is one flight during June in Alaska, a primary flight on the Californian coast from February to April, with a second partial flight from May to June. They can be found inhabiting open oak woods in hills, orchards, fields, meadows, stream courses, and canyons.

Genus:
  Anthocharis
Common names:
  Sara Orangetip
Size:
  32 to 44 mm (1¼ to 1¾ in.)
Male or female specimen:
  Male
Locality:
  Alaska coast south to Baja California mainly to west of Pacific divide
Host plants:
  Mustards
Conservation status:
  Not protected

Appias · Epaphia

Description

The male and female of this species are totally different. The male is white with a black edging to its forewing, while the female is mostly black with a white base to the hindwing and a white bar and spots on the forewing. They favor open bush and woodland areas, where they breed on *Capparis, Boscia, Niebuhria,* and members of the *Capparidaceae* family. It is quite common and can usually be found in large numbers.

Genus:
  Appias
Common names:
  Diverse White
Size:
  60 mm (2⅜ in.)
Male or female specimen:
  Male
Locality:
  Africa
Host plants:
  Capparis, Boscia, Niebuhria and all members of the *Capparidaceae* family
Conservation status:
  Not protected

Appias · Hombroni

Description

The male of the *A. hombroni* is a light steely blue on the upperside, with darker veins on the underside. The female is the reverse, dark with lighter areas to the base of the wings. Males love to mud-puddle and frequent riversides and clearings.

Genus:
  Appias
Common names:
  None
Size:
  70 mm (2⅝ in.)
Male or female specimen:
  Male (underside)
Locality:
  Sulawesi
Host plants:
  Capparidaceae family
Conservation status:
  Not protected

Appias · Lalassis

Description

Unlike other members of the *Appias* genus the forewings are not so elegantly curved in the *A. lalassis*. The background color is a blue-white, and the apex of the forewings has a black edging. On the forewing are two small spots which are more intense on the underside. This butterfly can be found in Burma and the southeast of Asia.

Genus:
  Appias
Common names:
  None
Size:
  70 mm (1⅝ in.)
Male or female specimen:
  Male (underside)
Locality:
  Southeast Asia, Burma
Host plants:
  Capparidaceae
Conservation status:
  Not protected

Appias Celestina
(Common Migrant)
At least two subspecies are known of this strong flier, one of them being a silvery blue. The other is light orange in the middle of its wings, with a dark brownish-black on the outside. You are more likely to see the male of this species, which spends most of its time in the rainforest canopy.

Appias · Placida

Description

The *A. placida* is an extremely strong flier and inhabits river edges within the rainforest and clearings. It is very unusual in color, being dark brown to black, with no other markings with the exception of a pale cream border. Typical of this genus the forewings are quite curved and pointed. It is thought to feed on members of the *Capparidaceae* family.

Genus:
  Appias
Common names:
  None
Size:
  70 mm (2⅜ in.)
Male or female specimen:
  Male
Locality:
  Asia
Host plants:
  Capparidaceae family
Conservation status:
  Not protected

Artogeia · Napi

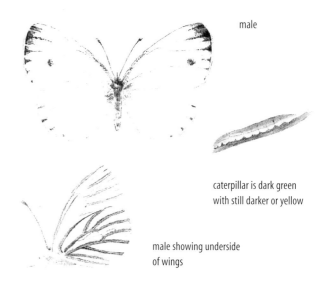

male

caterpillar is dark green with still darker or yellow

male showing underside of wings

Description

The Veined White can be found throughout the countryside, but prefers damp, sheltered areas. It breeds on wild crucifers and is not a pest of cabbage crops. The dusky vein markings on the undersides of the wings are variable in color and make it well camouflaged when it roosts among vegetation. It can be found across Europe (except for some Mediterranean islands), parts of North Africa, across Asia, and in North America. Its range is stable in most European countries. Adults occur widely but tend to congregate in damp, lush vegetation where their foodplants are found, especially hedgerows, ditches, banks of rivers, lakes, and ponds, damp meadows and moorland, and woodland ridges and edges.

Genus:
  Artogeia
Common names:
  Veined White, Green-veined White, Mustard White
Size:
  32 to 50 mm (1¼ to 2 in.)
Male or female specimen:
  Male
Locality:
  Europe, North Africa, Asia, United Kingdom and North America
Host plants:
  Cresses and toothworts
Conservation status:
  Not protected

Artogeia · Virginiensis

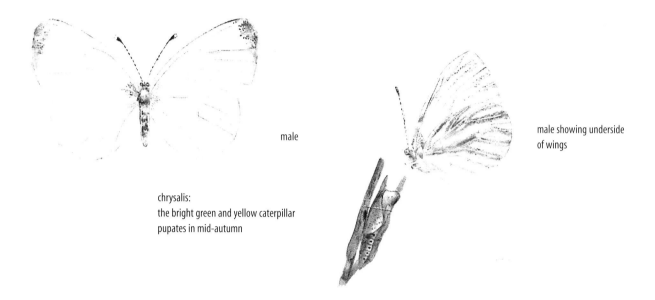

male

male showing underside
of wings

chrysalis:
the bright green and yellow caterpillar
pupates in mid-autumn

Description

The wings of the West Virginia White are translucent, whitish, with no yellowish tint underneath. The underside of the hindwings have light brown or pale gray scaling along veins. Males patrol slowly to locate females. Eggs are laid singly on undersides of host plant leaves. Chrysalids hibernate on stems or plant litter under the plant. In the North, they make one flight in May; while in the South, one flight from April to May. The adults feed on flower nectar from toothworts, spring beauty, violets, and other plants. This species is on the decline due to timbering, development, and spread of garlic mustard (*Alliaria officinalis*). but is not protected. The West Virginia White and the Mustard White were once thought to be the same species because they are so similar. Although it does have a plainer appearance than the Mustard White with no dark spots. They are typically found in the Great Lakes States along the Appalachians from New England to Alabama and southern Ontario and in moist deciduous forests.

Genus:
Artogeia
Common names:
West Virginia White
Size:
32 to 50 mm (1¼ to 2 in.)
Male or female specimen:
Male
Locality:
Northern Great Lakes states and from New England southwest along the Appalachians to north Georgia and northeast Alabama
Host plants:
Toothworts (*Dentaria diphylla* and *D. laciniata*) in the mustard (*Brassicaceae*) family
Conservation status:
Not protected

Ascia · Monuste

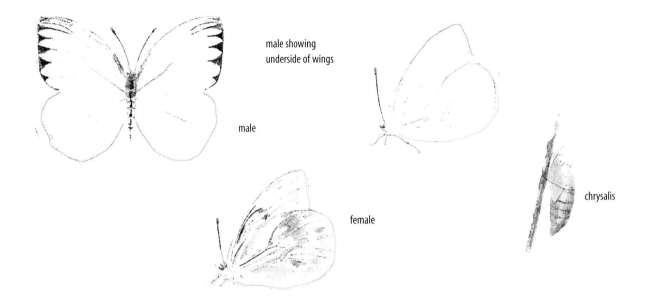

male showing underside of wings

male

female

chrysalis

Description

The male Great Southern White has white, pointed wings with charcoal scales dusting the tips and surrounding veins. The female is either like the male but with darker margins, or entirely suffused with smoky brown or gray scales. The caterpillar is either pale or bright yellow, striped greenish-maroon, and feeds on a wide array of cultivated and wild crucifers, capers, and saltworts, including pepper grass (*Lepidium virginicum*), saltwort (*Batis maritima*), and spider flower (*Cleome spinosa*). They favor beaches, salt marshes, coastal plains, offshore islands, and sandy flats. Because the striking dimorphism of the female depends upon the length of day, a higher proportion of the summer population is of a darker color. Generally common, the Great Southern White builds up to enormous numbers prior to northerly emigrations, which occur irregularly and are probably due to a local scarcity of food.

Genus:
Ascia
Common names:
Great Southern White
Size:
40 to 57 mm (1½ to 2¼ in.)
Male or female specimen:
Male and female
Locality:
Neotropics: southern Texas, Gulf Coast and Florida, emigrating up Mississippi Valley to Kansas and up Atlantic to Virginia
Host plants:
Crucifers and saltworts
Conservation status:
Not protected

Belenois · Aurota

Description

The *Belenois* are a genus of medium-sized African migratory butterflies. It is a powerful flier that can be seen dashing between date palms, across clearings, and over the ground where it frequently settles, often stopping to sip the nectar from flowers. It has been observed from mid-November to mid-April with three peaks—late November, mid- to late January, and late March.

The pale yellow conical, heavily ribbed eggs are laid in groups of up to 30 on the leaf underside of growing shoots with sometimes four batches per shoot. After a few days they turn orange and then, prior to emergence, gray. The larvae are grayish-green when young and covered in dark bristles, they are very gregarious. When fully grown they are mid-gray with a broad greenish-yellow dorsal band and a yellowish underside. Two very distinct features are the long pale, ventral hairs and small orange spots covering the whole body. Once they reach this size and color they are very inactive—spending much of their time sunbathing.

Genus:
  Belenois
Common names:
  Brown-veined White
Size:
  60 mm (2⅜ in.)
Male or female specimen:
  Male
Locality:
  From sub-Saharan Africa across Arabia to Syria, India and Sri Lanka
Host plants:
  Capparis and *Boscia* species
Conservation status:
  Not protected

Belenois · Thysa

Description

This butterfly lives in the rainforest and light woodland, and breeds off the plants of the *Capparidaceae*. Although both sexes have the same pattern on their wings, the background colors differ. It is white in the male and ocher in the female. The undersides of the hindwing are orange, which shows through slightly to the upper surface. Other distinguishing characteristics are the lack of a black spot on the forewing, and the triangular markings around the edges of the wings.

Genus:
  Belenois
Common names:
  False Dotted Border
Size:
  78 mm (3 in.)
Male or female specimen:
  Male
Locality:
  Africa
Host plants:
  Capparidaceae family
Conservation status:
  Not protected

Catopsilia · Pomona

male

female

Description

This butterfly comes in many different color forms, varying from fresh yellow to darker forms in the female. Underneath the wings are dirty white with dark orange markings. The caterpillar is green with a dark dorsal stripe, and has a pale green head with black dots. It usually rests lying along the midrib of a leaf, making it very hard to see. The pupa is also hard to see as it closely resembles a leaf. The eggs are pale yellow and barrel-shaped with ribs. They are laid singly on leaflets of the foodplant. This species can also be found in parts of northern and southern Australia.

Genus:
  Catopsilia
Common names:
  Lemon Migrant, Lemon Emigrant
Size:
  80 mm (3⅛ in.)
Male or female specimen:
  Male and female
Locality:
  Madagascar and Mauritius through India to Japan
Host plants:
  Cassia species and *Butea frondosa*
Conservation status:
  Not protected

Colias · Alexandra

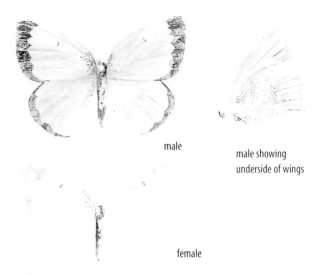
male

male showing underside of wings

female

Description

The upper surface of the male is bright yellow with pale yellow at the wing bases. The wings are edged by a narrow black border crossed by yellow veins, with a small cell spot. The female is yellow, sometimes white, with forewing border faded or absent. The underside of the hindwing of both sexes is green-gray; the cell spot is white with no surrounding ring. Males patrol open areas for females. Eggs are laid singly on top of host plant leaves. There is one flight from May to August. Adults feed on the nectar of flowers including blanket flower, and milk vetches. They can be seen along road edges, fields, meadows, and sagebrush flats. This species is demonstrably secure globally, although it may be quite rare in parts of its range.

Genus:
  Colias
Common names:
  Queen Alexandra's Sulphur
Size:
  40 to 51 mm (1½ to 2 in.)
Male or female specimen:
  Male and female
Locality:
  British Columbia south and east to eastern California, Arizona and New Mexico
Host plants:
  Legumes such as wild pea and locoweed
Conservation status:
  Not protected

Colias · Behrii

Description

This is quite a small sulfur that has a dull green upper surface in the male with a darker border, and a pale hindwing cell spot. The female is greenish-yellow with a dark diffuse border. The underside of both sexes are green. The males tend to patrol low to the ground in their search for females, and favor subalpine and alpine meadows. They have one flight from July to August. The female lays her eggs on willow and blueberry, plants that are typical of wetter habitats.

Genus:
  Colias
Common names:
  Sierra Green Sulphur
Size:
  44 mm (1¾ in.)
Male or female specimen:
  Male
Locality:
  Isolated range in California's Sierra Nevada from Tuolumne County south to Tulare County
Host plants:
  Low blueberries (*Vaccinium* species) in the heath family (*Ericaceae*) and gentian (*Gentiana newberryi*)
Conservation status:
  Not protected but threatened throughout its range

Colias · Croceus

Description

This butterfly is far reaching and is commonly found on the south coast of England and Wales from May to October time in open country, waysides and flowered areas. Numbers tend to fluctuate with times of increased sightings remembered as 'Clouded Yellow Years.' As they fly so fast they are difficult to photograph and they settle only very briefly to get nectar. The undersides of the wings are a greenish yellow, while the upper surfaces a brighter orange/yellow with a thick black border. The female Colias Croceus is duller in than the male, although some of its markings are stronger.

Genus:
  Colias
Common names:
  Clouded Yelow
Size:
  55mm (2 ⅛in)
Male or female specimen:
  Male
Locality:
  Palearctic and Oriental regions
Host plants:
  Not known
Conservation status:
  Not protected

Colias · Eurytheme

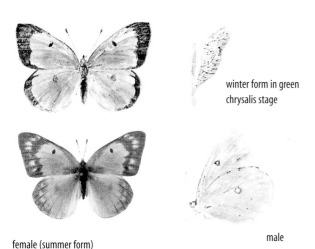

winter form in green chrysalis stage

female (summer form)

male

Description

One of the most common and widespread of the *Colias* species is the Orange Sulfur. It is a yellow species with some orange on the upperside and some small dark dots on the forewing. The underside of the hindwing has a silver spot that is pink-rimmed. It feeds on alfalfa and other legumes and is in flight from June to October. Males patrol for receptive females, who lay eggs singly on top of host plant leaves. Most feeding takes place at night, when young caterpillars chew holes in the tops of leaves, then later feed from the leaf tip. Older caterpillars eat half of the leaf before moving to the other half. Adult butterflies feed on the nectar from many kinds of flowers including dandelion, milkweeds, goldenrods, and asters. They can be seen in a wide variety of open sites, especially clover and alfalfa fields, mowed fields, vacant lots, meadows, and road edges. No protection of this species is needed, though the caterpillars can be very destructive in alfalfa fields.

Genus:
  Colias
Common names:
  Orange Sulphur
Size:
  40 to 65 mm (1½ to 2½ in.)
Male or female specimen:
  Male and female
Locality:
  Southern Canada to central Mexico, coast to coast in the United States except for the Florida peninsula
Host plants:
  Legumes particularly alfalfa and clover
Conservation status:
  Not protected

Colias · Hecla

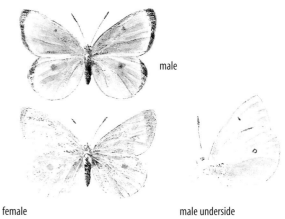

male

female

male underside

Description

Because this butterfly lives in a cold climate, the species often takes two years to complete its life cycle, overwintering in either the caterpillar or chrysalis form. The wings are either a dull orange or yellow, and fringed with pink. The underside of the hindwing is dusky green, usually with an elongated pink discal spot. The caterpillar is green with tiny black spots and a light lateral line along each side. There is one flight from late June to mid August. Truly holoarctic, this butterfly skirts the Arctic Circle around the globe. It is one of only about half a dozen butterflies resident in Greenland. Living on the margins of human habitability, it flits quickly and low over the tussocks and lichen-encrusted stones of the Northland.

Genus:
  Colias
Common names:
  Greenland Sulphur
Size:
  40 to 50 mm (1½ to 2 in.)
Male or female specimen:
  Male and female
Locality:
  Holoarctic: Greenland coast, northern Canada, northern and eastern Alaska, Yukon and British Columbia
Host plants:
  Astragalus, Amoria, Arctostaphylos, Vaccinium
Conservation status:
  Not protected

Colias · Nastes

male   male underside

Description

The upperside of both sexes is dirty white or dirty green-yellow, with a black border containing white or greenish spots. The underside of the hindwing has submarginal rows of black spots. This species overwinter as mature caterpillars. They have one flight from late June to early August. This butterfly may be found on bogs, moors, and in tundra habitat where its foodplant, alpine milk vetch, is abundant. Adults fly rapidly and very erratically over the tundra, dropping between rocks to hide.

The caterpillar is green with red-edged side stripes. This species is restricted to the tundra and alpine zones stretching from northern and western Alaska across northern Northwest Territories and the Arctic islands, southward through British Columbia to northern Washington and northern Montana.

Genus:
  Colias
Common names:
  Arctic Green Sulphur, Pale Arctic Clouded Yellow, Labrador Sulphur
Size:
  48 mm (1⅞ in.)
Male or female specimen:
  Male
Locality:
  Alaska south in Rocky Mountains to north-central Washington and northwest Montana
Host plants:
  Plants of the pea family (*Fabaceae*) including milk vetch (*Astragalus alpinus*) and white clover (*Trifolium repens*)
Conservation status:
  Not protected

Colias ·Palaeno

Description

Often found in Subarctic bogs, taiga openings and arctic tundra in the North American region. It's a pretty specimen with pink fringes and wide black borders on its upper wings and a dusky green coloring on the underside of its hind wing. The females tend to be lighter with more distinctive markings than the males. They fly from the middle of June to early August.

Genus:
 Colias
Common names:
 Palaeno Sulfur, Chippewa Sulfur
Size:
 50 mm (2 in.)
Male or female specimen:
 Male
Locality:
 Nearctic and Palearctic regions
Host plants:
 Not known
Conservation status:
 Not protected

Colias · Scudderi Gigantea

Description

This butterfly can be found in mountain meadows and willow bogs from Alaska south through the Rocky Mountains to northern New Mexico. The upper surface of the male is lemon yellow with a wide, dark border cut by yellow veins. The females are often white, with small black cell spots; the border is usually incomplete or lacking. Underside of both sexes are dirty green. Males patrol near willows for receptive females. The females lay eggs singly on young host plant leaves, and the young caterpillars eat the leaves. Second-, third-, and fourth-stage caterpillars hibernate. They have one flight from late June to August. This species is quite secure globally.

Genus:
 Colias
Common names:
 Willow Sulphur
Size:
 50 mm (2 in.)
Male or female specimen:
 Male
Locality:
 Alaska south through Rocky Mountains to northern New Mexico
Host plants:
 Willow shrubs in the willow family (*Salicaceae*)
Conservation status:
 Not protected

Colotis · Danae

Description

The coloring of these butterflies is quite varied and differs between the two sexes, with the exception of the scarlet tips. The background color of the male is white with wings edged entirely in black. However, on the female the white is covered with a faint row of black spots and the base of the wings are gray. Also the scarlet wing tips on the female have a row of black spots, and black scales intrude gradually from the margin. The *C. danae* lives along the edges of woodland, in bush and savannah country, and breeds on the *Cadaba* species that belongs to the *Capparidaceae* family.

Genus:
   Colotis
Common names:
   Scarlet Tip, Crimson Tip
Size:
   50 mm (2 in.)
Male or female specimen:
   Male
Locality:
   Africa and Asia
Host plants:
   Capparidaceae
Conservation status:
   Not protected

Colotis · Eris

Description

The markings in this butterfly are similar on both sexes, but the background colors differ. The male is white while the female has a cream ground color. The black markings are very strong toward the edge of the forewing and around the apex of the wing. The male also has some brown marks, but these are much smaller and cream in color on the female. Their habitat is open bush areas and the savannah, and it breeds on its host plant—various members of the caper family.

Genus:
   Colotis
Common names:
   Banded Gold Tip, Black-barred Gold Tip
Size:
   55 mm (2⅛ in.)
Male or female specimen:
   Male
Locality:
   Africa
Host plants:
   Caper family
Conservation status:
   Not protected

Delias · Eucharis

Description

This is a beautiful white butterfly with crimson colored spots and a bright yellow patch on the underside of the hindwing. In the female, the forewing apices are more rounded and the black scales along the veins and the intervening spaces are more extensive, giving the butterfly a grayish appearance. It is a very common, widely distributed butterfly from sea level to the highest elevations and is found everywhere—in cities, villages, cultivated areas, home gardens, forests, just about anywhere that has trees that supports its parasitic larval host plant *Loranthus*.

It is a striking butterfly, easily identified on the wing by its bright contrasting colors. It is also a warning to predators that may think of making a meal of it. It is a poisonous species and flies leisurely and slowly, well aware that its unpalatable qualities do not warrant speed or agility. Since they spend their entire life in the canopy of trees, they could be dislodged and killed by strong gusts of wind. However, they have a counter-measure to prevent such accidents. When dislodged, they remain connected to the leaves by hanging from strong silky threads produced by their salivary glands, and once the winds calm down, they climb up to safety using these threads.

Genus:
 Delias
Common names:
 Common Jezebel
Size:
 83 mm (3⅛ in.)
Male or female specimen:
 Male (underside)
Locality:
 Asia
Host plants:
 Loranthus
Conservation status:
 Not protected

Euchloe · Hyantis

Description

A small white butterfly with green marbling underneath, it is found only in the spring. The upperside of the forewing has a cell bar (usually devoid of white scales) very close to the edge of the wing. The underside is pearly white; and the hindwing has green marbling. Males patrol near host plants or on hilltops for receptive females. Eggs are laid singly on host plant leaves and there is one single flight from March to June. The adult butterflies feed on flower nectar including that of hosts and others such as phloxes. Their habitat is deserts, rocky canyons, hills, ridges, and open woodlands.

Genus:
 Euchloe
Common names:
 Pearl Marblewing
Size:
 35 mm (1⅜ in.)
Male or female specimen:
 Male
Locality:
 Baja California north to British Columbia, east to Colourado and New Mexico
Host plants:
 Plants in the mustard (*Brassicaceae*) family including rock cress (*Arabis*), peppergrass (*Lepidium*), tansymustard (*Descurainia*) and jewel flower (*Streptanthus*) species
Conservation status:
 Not protected

Eurema · Daira

Description

The courtship behavior of this species is rather unusual. After landing just near the female, the male waves one of his forewings in front of the female antennae. This behavior may occur several times until the female accepts the male for copulation. The wing-waving display is a requisite part of successful courtship.

Males and females differ, plus they have two seasonal forms. The upperside of the male forewing is yellow with a black bar along the inner edge and a large black area at the apex. Females vary from yellow to white, forewing with gray-black on the apex and a black patch on the outer edge of the hindwing. In the summer (or the wet season) the form is smaller with more extensive black areas. The underside hindwing of the summer form is satiny white, while that of the winter form is brick red or tan with two small black spots in the cell. Males patrol open areas for females. Females lay single eggs on the terminal growth of host plants. Their habitat is tropical and subtropical dunes, pastures, and open pine woods.

male

male, also showing underside

female, also showing underside

chrysalis

Genus:
Eurema
Common names:
Fairy Yellow, Barred Sulphur
Size:
25 to 38 mm (1 to 1½ in.)
Male or female specimen:
Male and female
Locality:
Argentina north to the United States Deep South; stray to southern Arizona, South Dakota, South Texas and Washington, DC
Host plants:
Pencil flower (*Stylosanthes biflora*), joint vetches (*Aeschynomene* species) and other plants in the pea family (*Fabaceae*)
Conservation status:
Not protected

Eurema · Hecabe Solifera

Description

The Common Grass Yellow is often referred to as the most abundant butterfly in Malaysia and Singapore. The species can be found throughout Singapore, even in the heart of the city. They are active throughout the year and several generations are completed each year. Their flight is slow, erratic, and close to the ground. These butterflies live less than a week as adults, with the size of the adults varying with the seasons. Adults appearing in late summer to early fall are the largest and smaller adults appear as the dry season progresses. The caterpillar pupates on the stem of a plant and can closely resemble the stem or a fresh leaf, making it difficult to detect.

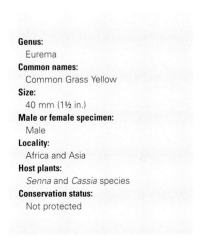

Genus:
 Eurema
Common names:
 Common Grass Yellow
Size:
 40 mm (1½ in.)
Male or female specimen:
 Male
Locality:
 Africa and Asia
Host plants:
 Senna and *Cassia* species
Conservation status:
 Not protected

Eurema · Lisa

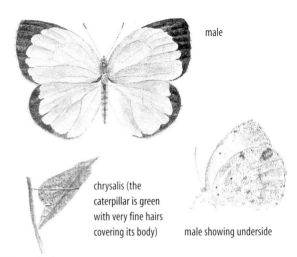

male

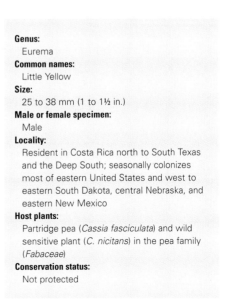

chrysalis (the caterpillar is green with very fine hairs covering its body)

male showing underside

Description

The Little Yellow is common throughout the eastern United States and can be found in dry, open areas including roadsides, sandy fields, abandoned fields, along railroad tracks, and occasionally open woods. The upperside of the male forewing is yellow with a wide black apex, and also a black border around the hindwing. The female is also yellow (rarely white) with black borders. Both sexes have a small black spot in the forewing cell. Males patrol for females during warm daylight hours. Females lay single eggs on midveins or between leaflets of host plant leaves.

Genus:
 Eurema
Common names:
 Little Yellow
Size:
 25 to 38 mm (1 to 1½ in.)
Male or female specimen:
 Male
Locality:
 Resident in Costa Rica north to South Texas and the Deep South; seasonally colonizes most of eastern United States and west to eastern South Dakota, central Nebraska, and eastern New Mexico
Host plants:
 Partridge pea (*Cassia fasciculata*) and wild sensitive plant (*C. nicitans*) in the pea family (*Fabaceae*)
Conservation status:
 Not protected

Eurema · Mexicana

Description

The Eurema Mexicana has a pleasant coloring combining white, yellow and brown. Its hindwing is light yellow with brown spots, but most distinctive of all is the outline of the dog's head on the forewing, a marking that is lacking on the female butterfly. It is often found in open, dry areas; flats, hillsides, deserts and prairies, or moister areas in Mexico and Central America.

Genus:
Eurema
Common names:
Mexican Yellow
Size:
50mm (2in)
Male or female specimen:
Male
Locality:
North to South America
Host plants:
Acacia and Diphysa from the pea family
Conservation status:
Not protected

Eurema · Nicippe

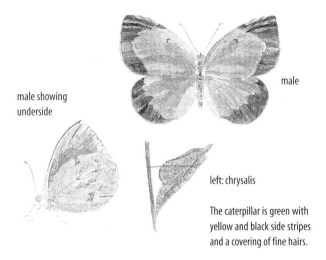

male showing underside

male

left: chrysalis

The caterpillar is green with yellow and black side stripes and a covering of fine hairs.

Description

The Sleepy Orange has earned its name by hibernating, in the adult stage, through the colder days of winter in its normal, southerly range. The upperside of the wings is orange in both sexes; the orange-yellow form is rare. The forewing has a small black cell spot. The male has sharply defined black borders on outer and costal margins; while the female borders are not so well-defined. In winter form, the underside of the hindwing is brick red, brown, or tan; in summer form it is orange-yellow. Males patrol flats and gullies for females. Females lay eggs singly under host plant leaves. There are four to five flights, all year long, in southern Texas and Deep South, and mid- to late summer in the North. They frequent low elevation areas including pine flats, fields, desert scrub, gardens, vacant lots, road edges, and washes.

Genus:
Eurema
Common names:
Sleepy Orange
Size:
32 to 50 mm (1¼ to 2 in.)
Male or female specimen:
Male
Locality:
Central America north to along the United States-Mexico border; vagrant to nonmountainous parts of the eastern U. S. south of 40° latitude; rare stray to Ontario, Connecticut, South Dakota and Colorado
Host plants:
Cassia species in the pea family (*Fabaceae*).
Conservation status:
Not protected

Ganyra · Buniae

Description

These powerful fliers are a genus of North and South America, and prefer to live in open areas. It is not dissimilar to the Cabbage White (*Pieris brassicae*) in appearance, although a little more blue in color. The male is completely blue-white with a dark margin. The females are generally darker and are often marked along the veins by brown scales. One interesting difference between the coloring of these butterflies is that those that migrate are gray, while the nonmigrating ones are yellow-white with dark margins.

Genus:
   Ganyra
Common names:
   None
Size:
   80 mm (3⅛ in.)
Male or female specimen:
   Male (underside)
Locality:
   North and South America
Host plants:
   Capparidaceae, Cruciferae and
   Tropaeolaceae
Conservation status:
   Not protected

Gonepteryx · Cleopatra

Description

The Cleopatra is a close relation of the Brimstone, *Gonepteryx rhamni*, but differs in having orange on its forewing. They hibernate as adults so you are most likely to see them in early spring and late summer. The female of the species is a pale green color. This butterfly is quite easy to spot on the wing, but is somewhat camouflaged when feeding. It can be seen flying around wooded and rural areas, and breeds on buckthorns and species of the *Rhamnus*.

Genus:
   Gonepteryx
Common names:
   Cleopatra
Size:
   65 mm (2½ in.)
Male or female specimen:
   Male (underside)
Locality:
   Europe and Africa
Host plants:
   Buckthorns and *Rhamnus* species
Conservation status:
   Not protected

Hebomoia · Glaucippe

Description

This is the largest of the pierid butterflies found in Asia, and can be seen flying around the fringe of primary or secondary forests. It is easy to identify this butterfly from the bright orange tips of the wings, which is common to both sexes. The female, however, tends to be seen less than the male. There are a number of subspecies known, and one of the most impressive is *H. glaucippe vossi* which has bright yellow hindwings. In contrast the underside is quite dull and mottled, and has the appearance of a leaf.

Genus:
Hebomoia
Common names:
Great Orange Tip
Size:
100 mm (4 in.)
Male or female specimen:
Male
Locality:
Asia
Host plants:
Species of *Capparidaceae*, *Crateva religiosa* and *Capparis moonii*
Conservation status:
Not protected

Ixias · Undatus

Description

The *Ixias* is a large genus of butterflies found from India through Malaya to the Philippines. In *I. undatus* the differences between the two sexes are quite striking. The male is a very rich egg-yolk yellow on its upper with a thin, dark margin around its wings. The tips of the forewings are very dark with bright orange flashes in the center. The female is not nearly so brightly colored, she is a very pale blue with a dark apex and margins. This butterfly can be seen flying in open clearings along rainforest rivers and also in secondary vegetation.

Genus:
  Ixias
Common names:
  None
Size:
  76 mm (3 in.)
Male or female specimen:
  Male
Locality:
  India, Malaya, Philippines, Australia
Host plants:
  Capparis species
Conservation status:
  Not protected

Kricogonia · Lyside

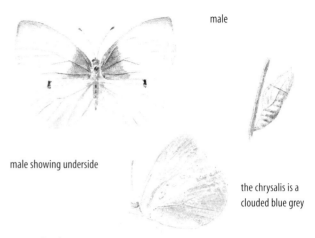

male

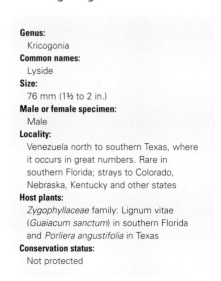

male showing underside

the chrysalis is a clouded blue grey

Description

The Lyside is commonly found in Texas but it favors tropical scrub lowlands and seasonally dry forests. The tip of the forewing is square-shaped. The upperside of the male is white with a yellow basal area, often with vertical black bars at the edges of the wing. The underside of the hindwing has raised veins and a satin sheen. Females occur in both yellow and white forms, and both sexes are extremely variable. The adults feed on the flowers of black mangrove and shepherd's needle in southern Florida. The caterpillars, which are green with gray to silver stripes rimmed in brown along the back, hide in bark crevices during the day and come out to feed after dark. Adults occasionally make huge migrations.

Genus:
  Kricogonia
Common names:
  Lyside
Size:
  76 mm (1½ to 2 in.)
Male or female specimen:
  Male
Locality:
  Venezuela north to southern Texas, where it occurs in great numbers. Rare in southern Florida; strays to Colorado, Nebraska, Kentucky and other states
Host plants:
  Zygophyllaceae family: Lignum vitae (*Guaiacum sanctum*) in southern Florida and *Porliera angustifolia* in Texas
Conservation status:
  Not protected

Neophasia · Menapia

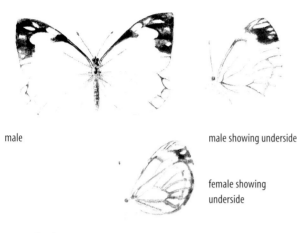

male

male showing underside

female showing underside

Description

Adults are daytime fliers and the males can be seen patroling near their host trees for females. The upperside of the forewing has a mostly all-white cell and black band along the costal margin. The underside of the hindwing has black veins. The female is very similar in appearance to the male but duller. Her hindwings often have red edges and are tinged with yellow. They lay their eggs stuck together in a row on a conifer needle. The caterpillars feed in groups when they are young and move apart when they are older. Caterpillars pupate at the base of the host tree after descending on a silken thread. There is one flight from June to September, and the adult butterflies feed on the nectar from the flowers of the rabbitbrush, and other yellow-flowered composites, and manarda.

Genus:
Neophasia
Common names:
Pine White
Size:
38 to 50 mm (1½ to 2 in.)
Male or female specimen:
Male and female
Locality:
British Columbia east to Alberta, south through Rocky Mountain states and California to Mexico; range just extends into western South Dakota and western Nebraska
Host plants:
Needles of various conifers including pines (*Pinus* species), Douglas-fir (*Pseudotsuga menziesii*) and true firs (*Abies* species)
Conservation status:
Not protected

Nepheronia · Thalassina

Description

A large butterfly characterized by combinations of white and yellow with black margins. They are mostly to be found in Africa, on woodland edges, but a species of the Nepheronia has been discovered in India. They are migrant butterflies and very strong fliers.

Genus:
Nepheronia
Common names:
Cambridge Vagrant
Size:
60mm (2 ⅜in)
Male or female specimen:
Male
Locality:
Africa and India
Host plants:
Not known
Conservation status:
Not protected

Pareronia · Valeria Hippia

Description

This butterfly is generally found at low elevations throughout India but abundantly in the forests of the Western Ghats. It prefers open forests with moderate rainfall, and visits flowers of *Ixora*, *Paveta*, and *Impatiens*. The males are light blue with black veins and a thick black margin all the way round the wings. The females are black with blue veining and a little speckling. This species can be found up to 3,000 ft. (900 m).

Genus:
  Pareronia
Common names:
  Wanderer
Size:
  38 to 50 mm (1½ to 2 in.)
Male or female specimen:
  Male
Locality:
  Asian region
Host plants:
  Capparis
Conservation status:
  Not protected

Parnassius · Clodius

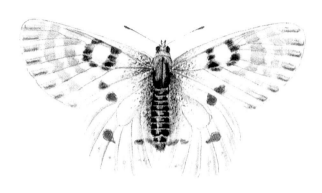

Description

This butterfly inhabits open woods, alpine areas, meadows, and rock outcrops. The upper surface of the forewing has a cell with three dark gray bars. The front wing has no red spots. The upper surface of the hindwing has two red spots, and females generally have a red anal bar. Mated females have large, white keeled pouches (*sphragis*) at the end of their abdomen.

Males patrol habitat to find females, and after mating they attach a pouch to the female to prevent multiple matings. Females lay single eggs scattered on the host plant. Caterpillars feed at night at the base of host plants and pupate in a loose silk cocoon above ground.

Genus:
  Parnassius
Common names:
  Clodius Parnassian
Size:
  56 to 79 mm (2¼ to 3 in.)
Male or female specimen:
  Female
Locality:
  Western Canada and western United States
Host plants:
  Bleeding heart family (*Fumariaceae*) including *Dicentra uniflora, D. formosa, and D. pauciflora*
Conservation status:
  Subspecies *strohbeeni* from California's Santa Cruz Mountains is now extinct

Phoebis · Agarithe

female

male

Description

The upper surface of the male Orange Giant Sulfur is, as its name suggests, bright orange with no markings. There are two female forms, pink-white or yellow-orange. The underside of the forewing of both sexes have straight submarginal lines. There are also two seasonal forms—the winter form has heavier underside markings. They fly all year in south Texas and south Florida, and stray north in mid- to late summer. The adults feed on nectar from flowers of lantana, shepherd's needle, bougainvilla, rose periwinkle, turk's cap, and hibiscus. They live in open, tropical lowlands including gardens, pastures, road edges, trails, and parks.

male showing

Genus:
  Phoebis
Common names:
  Orange Giant Sulphur
Size:
  56 to 72 mm (2¼ to 2¾ in.)
Male or female specimen:
  Male and female
Locality:
  Peru north to southern Texas and peninsular Florida. Rare stray to Colorado, South Dakota, Wisconsin and New Jersey
Host plants:
  Pithecellobium and *Inga* species in the pea family (Fabaceae)
Conservation status:
  Not protected

Phoebis · Avellaneda

Description

A rapid flying butterfly commonly found in montane woodlands. Distinguishing characteristics include a brown apical and postmedian band on the forewing, brown median band on the hindwing with darkened veins. The female has heavier markings.

Genus:
  Phoebis
Common names:
  Red-splashed Sulfur
Size:
  90mm (3 ⅝in)
Male or female specimen:
  Male
Locality:
  Neotropical region
Host plants:
  Not known
Conservation status:
  Not protected

Phoebis · Argante

Description

The habitat of this bright butterfly is in the disturbed areas in tropical forests, clearings, gardens, pastures, and road edges. The upperside of the male is bright orange with a black border on the forewing. Females vary from white to yellow, with dark or faded black borders. The underside of the hindwing of both sexes has broken, angled submarginal lines. The female lays her eggs singly on new leaves of the host plants, with many eggs placed on each plant. They fly all year in Central and South America, but stray to Texas from June to October. They feed on the nectar from a variety of red flowers. The species is demonstrably secure globally, though it may be quite rare in parts of its range, especially at the periphery.

Genus:
Phoebis
Common names:
Apricot Sulfur, Argante Giant Sulphur
Size:
74 mm (2⅞ in.)
Male or female specimen:
Male
Locality:
Paraguay north to Mexico. Reported very rarely (twice) in southern Texas and western Kansas
Host plants:
Shrubs and trees in the pea family (*Fabaceae*) including *Cassia*, *Pentaclethra* and *Inga* species
Conservation status:
Not protected

Phoebis · Philea

Description

These swift, high fliers favor open lowland sites such as gardens, forest edges, parks, and road edges. The upperside of the male is bright yellow-orange; the forewing has a red-orange bar and the hindwing has a red-orange outer margin. The two forms of the female, one off-white and the other yellow-orange, are much larger than the male. Both have an upperside of the forewing with solid black cell spots and a submarginal row of broken, angled black smudges. The outer half of the hindwing in the yellow form is red-orange. Females lay single eggs on leaves and flowers of their host plants, and the caterpillars prefer to feed on the flowers. Development is continuous in the wet season. There are two to three flights in Florida, one in the northern range from mid-late summer.

Genus:
Phoebis
Common names:
Orange-barred Sulphur, Yellow Apricot
Size:
90 mm (3½ in.)
Male or female specimen:
Male
Locality:
Brazil north to peninsular Florida and the Keys. Irregular wanderer to south Texas; extremely rare vagrant in Colorado, Minnesota, Wisconsin and Connecticut
Host plants:
Cassia species in the pea family (*Fabaceae*).
Conservation status:
Not protected

Phoebis · Sennae

Description

The fast-flying male of this species patrols disturbed open areas including parks, yards, gardens, beaches, road edges, abandoned fields, and scrub searching for receptive females. The upper surface of the male is lemon yellow with no markings. The female is yellow or white; with the outer edges of both wings having irregular black borders, and an upper forewing with a dark spot in the cell. The lower surface of the hindwing of both sexes has two pink-edged silver spots. The females lay their eggs singly on young leaves or flower buds of host plants, and the caterpillars eat leaves and rest on the underside of leaf petioles. There are many flights year round in the Deep South; and there may be one flight in late summer in other southern states; immigrants to northern states in August or September usually do not reproduce. Adults feed from the nectar from many different flowers with long tubes including cordia, bougainvilla, cardinal flower, hibiscus, lantana, and wild morning glory.

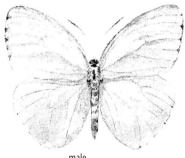

male

Genus:
Phoebis
Common names:
Cloudless Giant Sulphur
Size:
50 to 72 mm (2 to 2¾ in.)
Male or female specimen:
Male and female
Locality:
Permanent resident from Argentina north to southern Texas and the Deep South. Regular visitor and occasional colonist in most of the eastern United States and the Southwest
Host plants:
Cassia species in the pea family (Fabaceae)
Conservation status:
Not protected

Pieris · Napi

Description

An extremely variable species generally distributed in the Palaearctic and ranging to North America. A great number of geographical races inhabiting this region have been described, and the species also shows marked seasonal polyphenism. In particular, the spring generation is most strongly patterned. The veins are suffused with green, especially on the underside of the hindwing and more so in later generations. The female has more spots on the forewing than the male. The Green-veined White has one to three generations a year merging into each other, thus the butterfly appears on the wing practically from spring till fall. The caterpillar lives on wild crucifers (only rarely attacking crops), and the chrysalis hibernates for winter.

Genus:
  Pieris
Common names:
  Green-veined White, Sharp-veined White
Size:
  50 mm (2 in.)
Male or female specimen:
  Male
Locality:
  North and South America, Europe, Asia and into the Australian region
Host plants:
  Cruciferae
Conservation status:
  Not protected

Pieris · Rapae

above: The adult Cabbage White. These butterflies feast upon Buddleia and other summer flowers and then they turn their attentions to the cabbage patch.

below: The fully grown caterpillars seek walls and fences on which to pupate, but only a small proportion ever complete the transformation. Many of the caterpillars will have been visited by a little ichneumon called Apanteles glomeratus which will have laid its eggs inside the caterpillars and condemned them to death.

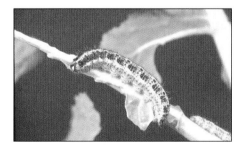

Pieris · Rapae

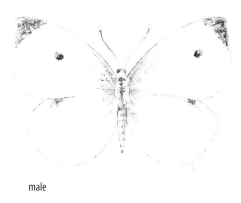

male

male showing underside

the pupae or chrysalises are yellowish with black spots and they are usually fixed vertically to the wall, held in place by a silken girdle or safety belt.

Description

The Cabbage White spread across the continent after accidental introduction from Europe into Quebec in 1860. It is the most successfully established butterfly in North America and is a destructive pest on cabbages, radishes, nasturtiums, and watercress. They first appear at the end of April, having passed the winter in the chrysalis stage. There are actually three species—the Large White, the Small White, and the Green-Veined White—all of which are widely distributed and common in the British Isles. The sexes are easily distinguished because the female has two black spots and a stripe on the upper side of each front wing, while the male is unmarked except for the black tips and leading edges of the wings. Adult butterflies emerge in August and their numbers are multiplied many times over by the swarms of immigrants which arrive from the continent at about this time.

Genus:
Pieris
Common names:
Cabbage White
Size:
32 to 44 mm (1¼ to 1¾ in.)
Male or female specimen:
Male
Locality:
From central Canada south through the United States (except Florida Keys, southern Louisiana and South Texas) to northwest Mexico, and the British Isles
Host plants:
Many plants in the mustard (*Brassicaceae*) family and occasionally some in the caper family (*Capparidaceae*)
Conservation status:
Not protected

Pontia · Chloridice

Description

The female of this species has more spotting than the male, and is slightly larger. Its common name, Small Bath White, comes from the British town of Bath in Somerset, where it was first depicted in a tapestry. Its other common name, Great Basin White, comes from one region where the butterfly occurs.

Genus:
  Pontia
Common names:
  Small Bath White, Great Basin White
Size:
  48 mm (1⅞ in.)
Male or female specimen:
  Male
Locality:
  From the Balkans and S. Russia across Asia Minor, Middle Asia and Kazakhstan to S. Siberia and Mongolia
Host plants:
  Various curciferous plants
Conservation status:
  Not protected

Pontia · Occidentalis

male   male showing underside

Description

The Western White inhabits mountain peaks, slopes, hilltops, railroad yards, open plains, and roadsides. The upperside of the forewing has marginal markings that are lighter than the submarginal stripe. The forewing tip and hindwing have veins outlined with gray-green. Short-day spring and fall forms have more prominent veins. Males patrol hilltops and ridges for receptive females. Females lay eggs singly on host plants, and the caterpillars will feed on leaves but prefer buds, flowers, and fruits. They have one flight from June to July in the far north; two flights from May to August in the South.

Genus:
  Pontia
Common names:
  Western White
Size:
  44 mm (1¾ in.)
Male or female specimen:
  Male
Locality:
  Alaska south to central California, northern Arizona and northern New Mexico; east to North Dakota and central Ontario
Host plants:
  Flowers and fruits of various members of the mustard (*Brassicaceae*) family
Conservation status:
  Not protected

Pontia · **Protodice**

female   male

Description

The male Common White patrols flats seeking receptive females, who lay eggs singly on leaves and flowers of host plants. Buds, flowers, and fruits are favorite foods of caterpillars, but they will also eat the leaves. A short-day form appears in spring and fall. The upperside of the male forewing has a black checkered pattern on the outer half. The female is more heavily patterned, but markings are more brown and diffuse. The hindwing of both the male and female is white, while the underside of the male hindwing has a pale checkered pattern. The underside of the female has yellow-tan markings on the hindwing and tip of the forewing. They can be seen in a wide variety of sites including dry weedy areas, vacant lots, fields, pastures, sandy areas, railroad beds, and roads.

Genus:
  Pontia
Common names:
  Common White, Chequered White
Size:
  32 to 50 mm (1¼ to 2 in.)
Male or female specimen:
  Male
Locality:
  Permanent resident in southern United States and northern Mexico; temporary in northern United States and southern Canada. Does not occur in most of New England
Host plants:
  Plants in the mustard family (*Brassicaceae*) including cabbage (*Brassica oleraceae*); and caper family (*Capparidaceae*) including Rocky Mountain bee-plant (*Cleome serrulata*)
Conservation status:
  Not protected

Family
Nymphalidae

This is the largest family of butterflies which contains around 5,000 species including Monarchs or Danaids, the Browns or Satyrids, and the Riodinids or Nemeobiids. Most of the common names of the subfamilies in *nymphalidae* seem to be derived from considerations of the adult butterflies. The "browns" are probably so-named simply because their basic wing color is brown. "Fritillary" is from the Latin—*fritillus* meaning "dice box." In Roman times, such dice boxes were embellished with checkered patterns, and the butterflies in this group have checkered black and brown patterns on their wings. The "Satyrs," "Nymphs," and "Danaids" may have been named for their similarities to legendary and mythical figures..

Acraea · Anemosa

Description

Both the male and female of this species are very similar, with a broad black border on the trailing edge of the hindwing. There is one distinguishing feature of the A. anemosa that makes it stand out from the others and that is the lack of tiny spots on the hindwing. The base of the wings are dark, and there are black marks on the forewings with a black tip. The underside of the hindwing has a lighter area in the middle. This butterfly favors open savannah and bush country, and can be seen throughout most of the year.

Genus:
  Acraea
Common names:
  Broad-bordered Acraea
Size:
  70 mm (2⅝ in.)
Male or female specimen:
  Male
Locality:
  Africa
Host plants:
  Daisy and passion flower family, Compositae and Passifloraceae.
Conservation status:
  Not protected

Acraea · Miranda

Description

Acraeas are attractive butterflies with rich tawny wings with *Acraeas* are attractive butterflies with rich tawny wings with black spots and wing borders. In some ways superficially resembling the *fritillaries* of more temperate climates, such as Europe, these butterflies are Afrotropical species with an elegant, strong flight. In the A. miranda the wings are quite long with a background color of orange-red. They do not have a black tip on the forewings as in other *acraeas*, but there are two curved bands on the forewing. This butterfly can be seen flying in the desert, keeping close to the ground, near scrubby vegetation.

Genus:
  Acraea
Common names:
  Desert Acraea
Size:
  55 mm (2⅛ in.)
Male or female specimen:
  Male (underside)
Locality:
  Africa
Host plants:
  Daisy and passion flower family, Compositae and Passifloraceae.
Conservation status:
  Not protected

Aglais · Milberti

male

The caterpillars begin this stage as communal-nest creatures but mature into loners that tend to roll leaves of host plants about themselves.

male underside

Description

The Milbert's Tortoiseshell has adapted to take advantage of every type of habitat that it encounters, and is possibly the longest lived of all North American butterflies. It has a squared-off tip to its forewing, and the upperside is black with a wide orange submarginal band which grades to yellow at the inner edge. There is a narrow black marginal border on both wings, and the hindwing border may contain some blue spots. In the afternoon, males perch on hillsides, banks of gulches, logs, or behind bushes to watch for females. Eggs are laid in large batches of up to 900 on the underside of host plant leaves. Adults feed in wet areas near woodlands, moist pastures, and marshes where they feed on the nectar of plants such as thistles, goldenrods, and lilacs.

Genus:
Aglais
Common names:
Milbert's Tortoiseshell, Fire-rim Tortoiseshell
Size:
51 mm (2 in.)
Male or female specimen:
Male
Locality:
North America south of the Taiga. Southern Alaska south to California, Nevada and New Mexico; east to Newfoundland and West Virginia
Host plants:
Nettles (Urtica dioica and U. procera)
Conservation status:
Not protected

Aglais · Urticae

Description

This butterfly is one of the most common to be found in the United Kingdom. Adults can be seen from around March to June with the new generation emerging mid-July when they can be spotted feeding on nectar-rich flowers in time for their winter hibernation period. The mating ritual of the Small Tortoiseshell involves a high speed chase between the male and female butterfly and the eggs are later laid on nettles. It is easily recognisable with its bright orange and back wings D-shaped blue spots.

Genus:
Aglais
Common names:
Small Tortoiseshell
Size:
50mm (2 in)
Male or female specimen:
Male
Locality:
Palearctic region
Host plants:
Nettles
Conservation status:
Not protected

Agrias · Amydon

Description

The *A. amydon* ranges from southern Mexico south through the Andes rainforests from Colombia to Bolivia, and east throughout much of the Amazon Basin, extending as far south as Iguazu Falls, Argentina. This beautiful butterfly is much sought after by collectors. It is a very powerful flier and varies considerably in color and markings. The uppers may be anything from blue, red, or orange, and the hindwing is mainly blue or brown. The underside of the hindwing is a little more consistent with convoluted curves of yellow or pale blue marks. This butterfly lives in the rainforest, with the male on the canopy often visiting fruit for their sugars.

Genus:
Agrias
Common names:
None
Size:
65 to 75 mm (2½ to 3 in.)
Male or female specimen:
Male
Locality:
South America
Host plants:
Genus *Erythroxylum*
Conservation status:
Not protected

Antanartia · Abyssinica

Description

This butterfly is found both on the continent as well as on the islands of Madagascar and Mauritius. It favors woods and forests in highland areas, where it likes to breed on the stinging nettle, *Urtica* species. Both sexes are similar in appearance, with a black-brown background color that is crossed by an orange-brown band. The forewing has black tips that are broken by a few white spots, and there is also an orange-brown band around the edge of the hindwing.

Genus:
Antanartia
Common names:
Ethiopian Admiral
Size:
56 mm (1½ in.)
Male or female specimen:
Male
Locality:
African region
Host plants:
Urtica, Acalpha and *Boehmeria* species
Conservation status:
Not protected

Antirrhaea · Geryon

Description

The *Antirrhaea* species come from the rainforests of South and Central America and are recognizable by their angular hindwings. They prefer the deep shade that is afforded by the forests and so has been difficult to study, but it is believed that they breed on a species of palm. The *A. geryon* is a large, brown butterfly which has quite a distinctive short tail which points to one side. There are also a row of large, false eyes on the margins of the wings. The underside is quite different in that it is a russet-gray with a line crossing both fore and hindwings.

Genus:
Antirrhaea
Common names:
None
Size:
93 mm (3½ in.)
Male or female specimen:
Male (underside)
Locality:
South America
Host plants:
Species of palm
Conservation status:
Not protected

Araschnia · Levana

above: Araschnia Levana (Map Butterfly) The underside of this butterfly gave it its
English name of the Map Butterfly. (See page 92 for more details.)

Araschnia · Levana

Description

This butterfly owes its English name to the map-like figures on the undersides of the wings. The differences between the first and the latter broods are quite remarkable (seasonal dimorphism). These differences are linked to the differences in temperature and duration of daylight to which the pupae are exposed in winter/spring and in summer. The upper sides of the wings of the first brood are brownish orange with black markings, while those of the second brood are dark brown with white discal bands. Map butterflies like shady places for their larval foodplants, where the female lays her eggs in chains on the underside of nettle leaves. The larvae live in companies and, like with most northern butterflies, the pupae hibernate. There are generally two, sometimes three broods from April to September.

Genus:
Araschnia
Common names:
Map Butterfly
Size:
38 mm (1½ in.)
Male or female specimen:
Male (underside)
Locality:
Europe and Asia
Host plants:
Urtica dioica and *Urtica urens*
Conservation status:
Not protected

Argynnis · Aglaja

Description

This is a large orange butterfly with black markings and a green suffusion on the underside of the hindwing. The underside also has a set of distinct, large, light-colored spots. It used to be widespread throughout the UK, but in recent years the numbers have declined quite considerably. It can still be seen in a variety of habitats, for example, moorland, downland, woodland, and along the coast. It is a very fast flier and it breeds on violets in clearings and in woods. There is usually only one brood each year.

Genus:
Argynnis
Common names:
Dark Green Fritillary
Size:
58 mm (2¼ in.)
Male or female specimen:
Male
Locality:
Europe and Asia
Host plants:
Viola tricolour, V. palustris, V. hirta
Conservation status:
Preserved or protected in some way

Asterocampa · Celtis

male

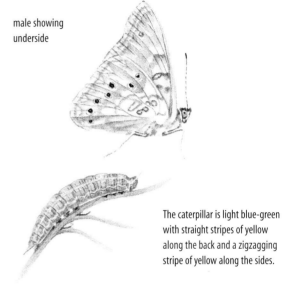

male showing underside

The caterpillar is light blue-green with straight stripes of yellow along the back and a zigzagging stripe of yellow along the sides.

Description

The Hackberry Butterfly is extremely variable geographically. The upperside is reddish brown and the forewing has one submarginal eyespot, a jagged row of white spots, and the cell has one solid black bar and two separate black spots. They fly in a fast and erratic manner, and rest upside down on tree trunks. Males perch on tall objects in sunny areas to watch for females. Eggs are laid in clusters, and the young caterpillars feed communally. Caterpillars overwinter in groups gathered inside dead rolled leaves. There are two broods from May–October. The first adults are usually on the wing by mid- to late April. Adults like to feed on sap, rotting fruit, dung, and carrion, and will take moisture at wet spots along roads and streams. They can be found along wooded streams, forest glades and river edges, wooded roadsides, and even in towns.

Genus:
Asterocampa
Common names:
Hackberry Butterfly
Size:
46 to 58 mm (1¾ to 2¼ in.)
Male or female specimen:
Male
Locality:
Eastern United States, central Plains states and the southwest mountains; northern Mexico
Host plants:
Various hackberries (*Celtis* species) and sugarberry (*Celtis laevigata*)
Conservation status:
Not protected

Asterocampa · Leilia

Description

The Desert Hackberry can be seen in thorn scrub, washes, canyons, and beside streams. The upperside is chestnut brown, and the forewing has two solid brown bars in the cell, median white spots, and two black eyespots near the outer margin. The males perch most of the day to watch for females. Eggs are laid in groups of 10 to 15 on the top of host plant leaves. Their flight is all year in south Texas, and April to November in Arizona. The adults feed on sap and dung, occasionally flower nectar and the species is secure globally.

Males of the Desert Hackberry butterfly occupy and defend perches adjacent to the larval foodplant. When returning from an interaction with a rival, the male will select a perch within about two square meters surrounding his original perch. These perching sites are surrounded by areas of significantly lower vegetation than other areas around the larval foodplant. Over the course of a morning the butterfly's behavior changes quite considerably. Early in the morning they perch on the ground with their wings open facing the sun. Later they perch facing the same direction, but with the wings closed. Later still they perch on vegetation a little less than a meter above the ground with their wings closed.

Genus:
  Asterocampa
Common names:
  Desert Hackberry
Size:
  65 mm (2½ in.)
Male or female specimen:
  Male
Locality:
  Southern Arizona east to south Texas, south to central Mexico
Host plants:
  Tree *Celtis pallida* in the elm family (*Ulmaceae*)
Conservation status:
  Not protected

Basilarchia · Archippus

male

male showing underside

The caterpillar (left) hibernates in leaf shreddings attached to a small branch. The chrysalis (right) resembles a bird dropping.

Description

The Viceroy mimics the Monarch butterfly over much of its range, but in the South it mimics the deeper-colored, but similarly distasteful Queen, thus gaining some protection from predators. The Viceroy's most notable feature is a black postmedian line across the hindwing both above and below. It is orange, veined with black, and a black border dotted with white spots above and white crescents below. It likes to be near or in wet meadows where willows grow on which it feeds, along with members of the rose family. It is double-brooded, appearing in early June and early August.

Genus:
Basilarchia
Common names:
Viceroy
Size:
79 mm (3 in.)
Male or female specimen:
Male
Locality:
North America
Host plants:
Salix, possibly populus
Conservation status:
Not protected

Basilarchia · Arthemis

Description

The White Admiral is a spectacular woodland butterfly, with white-banded black wings and a distinctive delicate flight—short periods of wing beats, followed by long glides. It is a fairly shade-tolerant butterfly, flying in dappled sunlight to lay eggs on Honeysuckle. It is black with a V-shaped band of stark white patches, and a submarginal double band of metallic blue crescents outside the orange band on the hindwing. Below, it is tan with white, orange, and blue bands from above showing through. The White Admiral occurs widely in southern Britain and has spread rapidly since the 1920s. The European range appears to be expanding northward, but there have been declines in several countries.

Genus:
   Basilarchia
Common names:
   White Admiral, Banded Purple
Size:
   79 mm (3 in.)
Male or female specimen:
   Male
Locality:
   Across central Europe from northern Spain to Turkey and as far north as Latvia, but absent from Scandinavia. Extends throughout Asia as far east as Japan
Host plants:
   Honeysuckle (*Lonicera periclymenum*)
Conservation status:
   Not protected

above: In autumn the caterpillar of the White Admiral wraps itself in leaves to make a protective casing, and it will spend the rest of the winter months in its homemade cocoon.

Basilarchia · Astyanax

male

male showing underside

Description

The Arizona Red-spotted Purple Butterfly is blue to blue-green with a lot of iridescence on the outer part of the hindwing. Its underside is typically dark brown. The butterfly often has several red-orange spots near the outer edges of its wings. It has a black body and a wing span that ranges from 2¼ to 4 in. (58 to 100 mm) in width. This butterfly is found throughout much of the United States including Arizona. It is usually found in deciduous or mixed forests, moist uplands, and valley bottoms. Adults eat sap, rotting fruit, carrion, dung, and occasionally nectar. The Red-spotted Purple is a mimic of the poisonous Pipevine Swallowtail. Females lay eggs singly on tips of host plant leaves which the caterpillars eat when they are born.

Genus:
   Basilarchia
Common names:
   Red-spotted Purple
Size:
   58 to 100 mm (2¼ to 4 in.)
Male or female specimen:
   Male
Locality:
   Most of the United States and Arizona
Host plants:
   Wild cherry, aspen, poplar, cottonwood, oaks, hawthorn, deerberry, birch, willows, basswood and shadbush
Conservation status:
   Not protected

The caterpillar (above) is off-white with darker patches. The chrysalis is mottled shades of brown.

Basilarchia · Lorquini

Description

The Lorquin's Admiral is a showy butterfly and quite large. This butterfly was named after Peirre Lorquin, an early French butterfly collector in California. It is brown-black on its dorsal wing with rows of white spots on both wings. A reddish patch occurs in the apical region of the lateral margin of the dorsal forewing. Like most butterflies the underside of the wings are much brighter than the top allowing them to confuse predators. This butterfly is usually associated with willows and moist riparian woodland vegetation. Adults often bask on protruding willow branches in sunny places. It has two broods—the first brood usually flies from April to June while the second brood is on the wing from August into October.

At first glance this butterfly can be confused with the California Sister. The orange of the Admiral's wings extends all the way to the edge whereas the California Sister has an orange spot that is nearly surrounded by black. Also the banding and coloration is different.

Genus:
Basilarchia
Common names:
Lorquin's Admiral, Orange Tip Admiral
Size:
70 mm (2⅝ in.)
Male or female specimen:
Male
Locality:
North America
Host plants:
Willow (*Salix* spp.)
Conservation status:
Not protected

male showing underside

Basilarchia · Weidemeyerii

male

male showing underside

Description

The Weidemeyer's Admiral is a fairly large butterfly with a black upperside and a white median band on both wings. The underside is brown with white markings repeated, the base of the hindwing is gray-white with dark crosslines, and the marginal spots on its hindwing are gray-white. This butterfly occurs along streams and rivers that are lined with willows or cottonwoods. It may occur in the mountainsides with nearby streams or in parklands, gardens, sand hills, and sagelands. Like some other members of the Brush-footed family, Weidemeyer's Admirals can be very territorial, chasing Mourning Cloak butterflies, Tiger Swallowtail butterflies, Crescentspot butterflies, or even Dragonflies from their territory. The males do not patrol their territories actively like some butterflies, instead, they perch in trees or shrubs to watch for competitors or receptive females. Females lay eggs singly on the tips of host plant leaves, and the caterpillars feed on the leaves. Third-stage caterpillars hibernate in shelters made of leaves, and this leaf "sleeping bag" is known as a hibernaculum. There are one to two broods per year, from late May or June through August or up to November during mild fall weather.

Genus:
Basilarchia
Common names:
Weidemeyer's Admiral
Size:
73 to 93 mm (2¾ to 3½ in.)
Male or female specimen:
Male
Locality:
Southern Alberta south to Nebraska and east-central California, southeastern Arizona and southern New Mexico
Host plants:
Aspen and cottonwood (*Populus*), willows (*Salix*), ocean spray (*Holodiscus*) and shadbush (*Amelanchier*)
Conservation status:
Not protected

Bassarona · Hikarugenzi

Description

This is an attractive butterfly in that its patterns are fairly uniform. It has a black-brown background with a curved band of white around the inside of the margin of the hindwing, which are scalloped, and one almost identical band on the forewing. There is also a scattering of smaller marks on the forewing.

Genus:
  Bassarona
Common names:
  None
Size:
  100 mm (4 in.)
Male or female specimen:
  Male
Locality:
  Philippines
Host plants:
  Little known
Conservation status:
  Not protected

Bassarona · Patala

above: Very little is known about the ecology of this species which exists as a number of subspecies from Northern India to China. It is a large butterfly with a wingspan of 120 mm (4l in.). It is a greenish-brown with strong yellow marks on its forewing. The picture above shows the underside of a male.

Bicyclus · Safitza

Description

The Common Bush Brown butterfly is found in rain forests, open glades and along paths, settling on leaves on the ground. It is predominantly brown but has a distinctive eye spot near the apex of its forewing. The female is duller in appearance.

Genus:
  Bicyclus
Common names:
  Common Bush Brown
Size:
  50mm (2in)
Male or female specimen:
  Male
Locality:
  Africa
Host plants:
  Poaceae
Conservation status:
  Not protected

Boloria · Eunomia

Description

The upperside of the Bog Fritillary is orange-brown to tan with dark markings. The underside of the hindwing is orange with light nonmetallic bands, and the postmedian row spots are white bordered with black. Males patrol in wet areas, for example bogs, moist tundra, and willow seeps, for females. Eggs are laid in groups of two to four under host plant leaves, which the caterpillars eat. Third- and fourth-stage caterpillars overwinter, and there is one brood from June to August. Adult butterflies feed on the nectar from flowers including Labrador Tea and Goldenrod.

Genus:
  Boloria
Common names:
  Ocellate Bog Fritillary, Bog Fritillary
Size:
  46 mm (1¾ in.)
Male or female specimen:
  Male
Locality:
  Alaska and most of Canada south to the bordering United States including northern Maine and the northern Great Lakes region; south in the Rocky Mountains to Colorado
Host plants:
  Willow (*Salix*), alpine smartweed (*Polygonum viviparum*) and violets (*Viola*)
Conservation status:
  Not protected

Boloria · Selene

Description

The Silver-bordered Fritillary is a common butterfly of wet meadows. It appears to be double-brooded and can be found from June to August. This and the Meadow Fritillary are easy for the novice butterflier to misidentify as they are about the same size, very active, and it is sometimes hard to get a good look at them before they fly. The upperside of the *B. selene* is bright orange and marked with black zigzags on the inner half of the wings. The outer portion of the wings is lined with a row of black dots, followed by a row of black triangles; the outermost edge is lined in black as well. Underneath, the forewing is yellowish orange and marked with black and brown. The hindwing has two rows of silver spots with a row of small black dots in between, and a scattering of silver patches near the base. It is generally found well inside the arctic regions and likes to visit woods, forest edges, alpine meadows, and bogs.

Genus:
  Boloria
Common names:
  Silver Meadow Fritillary, Small Pearl-bordered Fritillary
Size:
  42 mm (1⅝ in.)
Male or female specimen:
  Male (underside)
Locality:
  Europe and North America
Host plants:
  Violets (*Viola*)
Conservation status:
  Not protected

The caterpillar can be brownish or bluish-black, with black dots and patches, and may possibly appear mottled. It has a black head, an orangish line along the side, and yellowish spines tipped with black hairs. The spines towards the front are much longer than the rest. It can reach a maximum length of approximately 12.7 mm (H in.).

Brintesia · **Brahminus Wahminoides**

Description

This is a very dark brown butterfly which occurs widely in Europe and Asia. They tend to live in light woodland, but fly in sunny glades and between trees, laying their eggs on grasses such as the bromes (*Bromus*). The edges of its wings are distinctly scalloped in pale cream lunules. Stretching across the wings is a prominent cream band, which starts as an imperfect circle enclosing an indistinct eye spot on the tip of the forewing. As it reaches the rear it becomes a much more solid band. The undersides of this butterfly are much lighter than the uppers and the cream band is much more pronounced. They are very sensitive butterflies and immediately take off and fly high into trees when approached.

Genus:
  Brintesia
Common names:
  None
Size:
  65 mm (2½ in.)
Male or female specimen:
  Male
Locality:
  Europe and Asia
Host plants:
  Bromus
Conservation status:
  Not protected

Brintesia · **Circe**

Description

This butterfly is found in open woodlands and clearing and at a height of up to around 4,500 ft. It is an extremely powerful flyer taking itself across much of Europe, although it tends to prefer the hotter regions. The female is much larger and blacker with white median bands across its wings.

Genus:
  Brintesia
Common names:
  Great Banded Grayling
Size:
  65mm (2⅝ in)
Male or female specimen:
  Male
Locality:
  Palearctic region
Host plants:
  Poaceae
Conservation status:
  Not protected

Caerois · Gerdrudtus

Description

This genus of butterflies is very closely related to the *Antirrhaea*. The wings of the *C. gerdrudtus* have a very distinctive shape in that the forewing is very curved, while the hindwing is angular with quite a pronounced tail. On the upperside the background is a violet-blue, with a large eyespot on the forewing, and two much smaller ones on the hindwing. By contrast the undersides are quite pale and visibly crossed by veins. It is quite rare and lives and breeds in the rainforest.

Genus:
   Caerois
Common names:
   None
Size:
   104 mm (4⅛ in.)
Male or female specimen:
   Male (underside)
Locality:
   South and Central America
Host plants:
   Palm *(Socratea durisima)*
Conservation status:
   Not protected

Caligo · Memnon

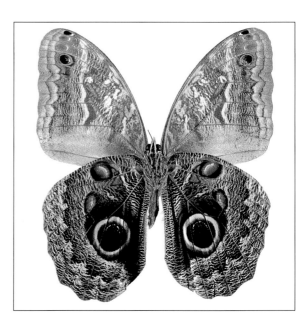

Description

The Owl Butterfly is one of Amazonia's largest species. The large eyespots on the wings serve either to scare a potential predator or to misdirect an attack away from the body (since predators will often first attack the eyes of prospective prey). This particular Owl Butterfly is quite easy to distinguish from the others by the large patch of pale orange-yellow covering most of the forewing. The outer area and the majority of the hindwing are dark. They live in agricultural areas where they breed on *Heliconia* species and the related banana.

Genus:
   Caligo
Common names:
   Owl Butterfly
Size:
   156 mm (6⅛ in.)
Male or female specimen:
   Male (underside)
Locality:
   South and Central America
Host plants:
   Banana family *(Musa)*
Conservation status:
   Not protected

Cercyonis · Pegala

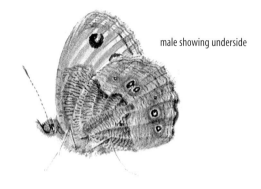

male showing underside

male

Description

The Large Wood Nymph can be found in much of North America. It is extremely variable, but generally has a brown background with quite distinct darker markings. Below it is brown streaked with many small bars of black, and there is a broad, cream-colored band with two spots of black with white and silver middles on the forewing. There are also scattered spots of black and white on the hindwing. As they perch on tree trunks or boughs to bask or drink sap, Large Wood Nymphs blend beautifully with the bark. When disturbed or seeking mates, they fly erratically through tall grasses, with little speed but great skill and endurance. Western wood nymphs visit such flowers as alfalfa and spiraea, while eastern populations seem to favor rotting fruit. There is only one brood—generally June to August or September.

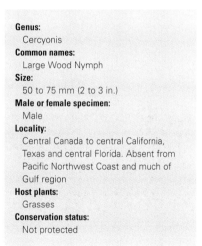

Genus:
Cercyonis
Common names:
Large Wood Nymph
Size:
50 to 75 mm (2 to 3 in.)
Male or female specimen:
Male
Locality:
Central Canada to central California, Texas and central Florida. Absent from Pacific Northwest Coast and much of Gulf region
Host plants:
Grasses
Conservation status:
Not protected

Cercyonis · Sthenele

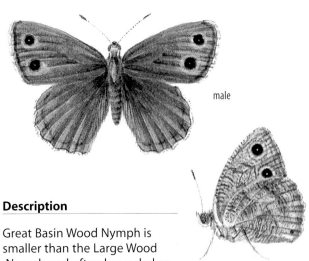

male

male showng underside

Description

Great Basin Wood Nymph is smaller than the Large Wood Nymph and often has a darker band within two dark lines across the hindwing. The upperside is brown, and the forewing of the male has two small eyespots, with the upper one larger. The female has two large eyespots of about the same size. These eyespots are of equal distance from the outer edge of the wing, and the dark basal half of the hindwing underside is separated from the lighter outer half by an irregular dark line. Males patrol all day to find females, who lay eggs singly on host plants. Caterpillars hatch and go into hibernation, not feeding until the following spring. They have one brood from June to August. They inhabit chaparral, oak woodland, open pine forest, juniper/pinyon woodland, and sagebrush.

Genus:
  Cercyonis
Common names:
  Great Basin Wood Nymph
Size:
  32 to 50 mm (1¼ to 2 in.)
Male or female specimen:
  Male
Locality:
  Central Canada to central California, Texas and central Florida. Absent from Pacific Northwest Coast and much of Gulf region
Host plants:
  Various grasses
Conservation status:
  Not protected

Cethosia · Chrysippe

Description

The Red Lacewing is a medium-sized butterfly found in Nepal, northeast India, Burma, Indochina, China, Thailand, and the Andaman Islands. The wings of the male are bright orange-red, and the margins are black with white spots. The wings of the female are black, brown, and gray with black and white spots on the black margins. The undersides of the wings are black, brown, and tan. The caterpillar has black and red stripes, and a black head and legs, with many black spikes emanating from the body. It lives only on the host plant *Passiflora cochinchinese*, which is a poisonous vine. The adult butterfly drinks nectar from *Lantana camara*.

Genus:
  Cethosia
Common names:
  Red Lacewing
Size:
  100 mm (4 in.)
Male or female specimen:
  Male
Locality:
  Nepal, northeast India, Burma, Indochina, China, Thailand and the Andaman Islands
Host plants:
  Passiflora cochinchinese
Conservation status:
  Not protected

Cethosia · Hypsea

Description

A forest species, the Malay Lacewing is one of the several Lacewing butterflies found in Malaysia. The fine, serrated pattern along the edge of their wings together with a combination of red, orange, brown, or white colors make them very attractive butterflies. It is bright orange-red above with broad black borders. The wings are scalloped, giving the hindwings an almost sawtoothlike appearance. The undersides are orange-red with white fasciae and are spotted with black forming an intricate pattern which probably gives the origin of its name "Lacewing." This butterfly is quite common in the nature reserves and can be found fluttering around flowering bushes like Prickly Lantana (*Lantana camara*) and the Snakeweed (*Stachytarpheta indica*). The wine red caterpillar has long spines and is known to feed on Passion Fruit vine.

Genus:
  Cethosia
Common names:
  Malay Lacewing
Size:
  88 mm (3⅜ in.)
Male or female specimen:
  Male
Locality:
  Malaysia
Host plants:
  Passion Fruit vine (*Adenia* spp.)

Conservation status:
  Not protected

Cethosia · Cyane

Description

This butterfly inhabits upland and lowland rain forests in South Asia. Its upper side is a rich reddish tawny color and distinctive markings include a black border with wavy white ribbon detailing and flashes of white near the tops of wings. The female is similar to the male but the tawny ground color is replaced by a dusky white hue and its underside is much paler in comparison.

Genus:
  Cethosia
Common names:
  Leopard Lacewing
Size:
  100 mm (4 in.)
Male or female specimen:
  Male
Locality:
  Oriental (South Asia)
Host plants:
  Passifloraceae or violales

Conservation status:
  Not protected

Charaxes · Boueti

Description

This is a typical member of the subfamily *Charaxinae*. It is a very large and robust butterfly which is extremely difficult to observe, as they fly high up in the forest and on savannah tree edges. They only come down to ground level for short periods of time, where their intense dorsal colors are instantly hidden by the cryptic and more matt colors of the underside. They do not feed on flowers like most other species, they prefer fermenting fleshy fruits like bananas, paw-paw, and mangoes. They have been seen jostling each other with their forewings, not unlike sparring birds, and if one has a close scrutiny of their forewings you will be surprised to see miniscule, yet well-developed teeth, on the costal margins.

Interestingly, it has a closely-linked relationship with a rare and uncommon bird, the Pied Mannikin (*Spermestes fringilloides*) whose own preferred diet of the seeds of bamboo have accounted for its localized distribution.

Genus:
   Charaxes
Common names:
   Red Forest Charaxes
Size:
   80 mm (3⅛ in.)
Male or female specimen:
   Male
Locality:
   African region
Host plants:
   Bindura or Wild Bamboo

Conservation status:
   Not protected

Charaxes · Castor

Description

This beautifully marked butterfly is found in woodlands and associated brush in Africa. The males are territorial and can usually be spotted on hilltops. The female shares the same blackish brown ground color but has larger forewing bands. Charaxes Castor larvae has been known to feed on the leaves of the Erythrina, or the Lucky Bean Tree, native to Africa.

Genus:
   Charaxes
Common names:
   Giant Charaxes
Size:
   110mm (4⅜ in)
Male or female specimen:
   Male
Locality:
   African region
Host plants:
   Erythrina

Conservation status:
   Not protected

Charaxes · **Protoclea**

Description

This is possibly South Africa's most spectacular *Charaxes*. It has been discovered that the true stronghold of this butterfly is really in Tembe Elephant Park, deep in an area of sand forests and wetlands in northern Tongaland, and this is probably due to the abundance of their foodplant, the Pod Mahogany (*Afzelia quanzensis*). The best months to see this butterfly seem to be from April through to June. The two sexes are completely different in appearance. The male is covered mostly in black with a wide margin of orange around the hindwing, which also has two little blue spots visible near the margin. The female, which is slightly larger, has a big band of white going across the wing which breaks up near the black tip of the forewing.

Genus:
  Charaxes
Common names:
  Flame-bordered Charaxes
Size:
  90 mm (3½ in.)
Male or female specimen:
  Male
Locality:
  South Africa
Host plants:
  Afzelia and *Zyzgium* species

Conservation status:
  Not protected

Chlosyne · **Gorgone**

Description

This butterfly inhabits open areas including ridges, prairies, streamsides, open hardwood forests, old fields, and forest edges. Its common name, Great Plains Checkerspot, was derived from the American Great Plains. Its upperside is orange with black markings, while the hindwing has a submarginal row of solid black spots. The underside of the hindwing has a zigzag pattern of brown and white bands and a median band of white chevrons. Males perch or patrol to find females, who lay their eggs in clusters on the underside of host plant leaves. There is one brood in the north from July to August, two broods in the central part of the range from May to September, and three broods in the south from April to September.

Genus:
  Chlosyne
Common names:
  Great Plains Chequerspot
Size:
  40 mm (1½ in.)
Male or female specimen:
  Male
Locality:
  North America
Host plants:
  Asteraceae including sunflower (*Helianthus*) and crosswort (*Lysimachia*) species

Conservation status:
  Not protected

Chlosyne · Lacinia

male

female

Description

This butterfly is quite variable and has a black upperside with a very wide orange or cream median band and small orange or white postmedian spots. The underside of the hindwing is black with a yellow to cream-colored median band, small white postmedian spots, and large cream-colored marginal spots. There is a red spot near the abdomen which is usually separate from the median band. During the day, males patrol around host plants or patrol and perch on hillsides in search of females. The eggs are laid in large groups on the underside of host plant leaves. Young caterpillars are gregarious and eat the underside of leaves; older caterpillars are solitary and eat leaves and stems. These butterflies inhabit pinyon or oak woodlands, thorn forest, desert hills, fields, road edges, and fencerows.

Genus:
Chlosyne
Common names:
Bordered Patch
Size:
40 to 50 mm (1½ to 2 in.)
Male or female specimen:
Male
Locality:
Argentina north through Mexico to Texas and southeastern New Mexico, west through Arizona to southern California, north to southeastern Nevada. Casual migrant to Colorado, Nebraska and Kansas; rarely to western Missouri
Host plants:
Sunflowers (*Helianthus*), ragweed (*Ambrosia trifida*), crownbeard (*Verbesina*) and cockleburs (*Xanthium*)

Conservation status:
Not protected

Cirrochroa · Thais Lanka

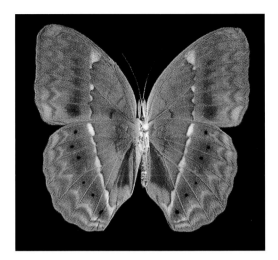

Description

The *C. thais lanka* is found in the lowland rainforests in India and Sri Lanka and a useful guide to identification is the poorly defined antennal club. The basic color of the wings is a rich browny-orange, with a small white dot on the leading edge of the forewing. There is a dark margin on the tip of the forewing and also on the edges of all the wings. The underside is a pearly purple-orange, with an occasional white line. The life history of this forest butterfly is still unknown.

Genus:
Cirrochroa
Common names:
None
Size:
70 mm (2⅝ in.)
Male or female specimen:
Male
Locality:
India and Sri Lanka
Host plants:
Not documented
Conservation status:
Not protected

Clossiana · Bellona

male

Description

The male of the Meadow Fritillary, as its name suggests, patrols meadows with a low flight, during warm daytime hours. Females lay eggs on twigs and plants other than the host violets. Caterpillars like to feed on violet leaves and hibernate when in the third to fourth stage of development. The forewing is distinctively squared off just below the tip, and the upperside is orange-red with heavy black markings. The underside of the hindwing is patterned with orange and purple-brown with a metallic dusting. There are two to three broods from late April to mid-October. Their favorite nectar sources are composites, including black-eyed susans, dandelions, and ox-eyed daisy. They tend to frequent wet places like meadows, pastures, hayfields, bogs, marshes, and wet aspen groves. Due to its adaptability to disturbed habitats, this butterfly is expanding its range southward from the southeastern states.

Genus:
Clossiana
Common names:
Meadow Fritillary
Size:
32 to 50 mm (1¼ to 2 in.)
Male or female specimen:
Male
Locality:
Eastern British Columbia east through southern Canada and northern United States to Newfoundland; south to northcentral Oregon, central Colorado, northeast Tennessee and northwest North Carolina
Host plants:
Violets including northern white violet (*Viola pallens*) and woolly blue violet (*V. sororia*)
Conservation status:
Not protected

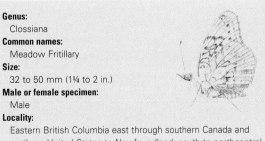

Clossiana · Epithore

male

left: The Western Meadow Fritillary succeeds in a variety of lowland and highland habitats, but favours sunny openings in mixed evergreen and deciduous mountain forests, maritime marshes, roadsides and lush meadows.

Description

The upperside of this butterfly is bright orange with zigzagging bands of dull black, with one circular patch open in the center of the body on the forewing. It has a broken band of thin white along the margins above. It is brown-orange with a similar black pattern on the forewing, and there are mottled shades of brown on the hindwing below. The Western Meadow Fritillary is a successful colonizer that can adapt to a wide variety of habitats, from meadows and roadsides to forest clearings and bogs. It can be abundant in some regions and regularly visits flowers, yellow ones being preferred. It has a slow zigzagging flight.

Genus:
Clossiana
Common names:
Western Meadow Fritillary
Size:
32 to 44 mm (1¼ to 1¾ in.)
Male or female specimen:
Male
Locality:
Central British Columbia and SW. Alberta south to central California and Idaho
Host plants:
Blueberry and bearberry
Conservation status:
Not protected

Clossiana · Euphryosyne

Description

The Pearl-bordered Fritillary can be found as early as April in open woodland areas or rough hillsides. It used to be known as the April Fritillary in England because of this, although it rarely flies so early there anymore. It is distinguishable from the Small Pearl-bordered Fritillary as it has a single pearl in the middle of the underside of the hindwing and yellow spots on the rest of the band. The female is duskier in coloring.

Genus:
Clossiana
Common names:
Pearl-bordered Fritillary
Size:
45mm (1⅞ in)
Male or female specimen:
Male
Locality:
Palearctic region
Host plants:
Viola (violet)
Conservation status:
Not protected

Clossiana · Freija

male

male showing underside

Description

Freija's Fritillary is a lovely butterfly that is associated with raised bogs. In south Finland they have either vanished or become exceedingly rare, due to peatland drainage. Freija's Fritillary is named for the Nordic goddess of love and beauty. The background color is a brownish orange with zigzagging bands of black and rows of black spots. It has an orange forewing, yellow-brown with scalloped bands of red and white, and there is a large, white patch near the center and a submarginal band of white patches below. The eggs are light brown, and the caterpillar is mottled brown with darker spines. The chrysalis is also a mottled brown. The harsh winter months of the North are spent in the mottled brown caterpillar stage. Freija's Fritillary is one of the earliest of the lesser fritillaries to be seen in Canada. In the southern part of its range in the west it is flying in mid-May. However, it flies in June and July in the Arctic. Although mainly considered a willow-bog species, this butterfly wanders into forest clearings and alpine valleys in search of flowers and is locally common on the tundra.

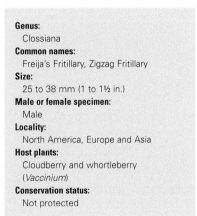

Genus:
  Clossiana
Common names:
  Freija's Fritillary, Zigzag Fritillary
Size:
  25 to 38 mm (1 to 1½ in.)
Male or female specimen:
  Male
Locality:
  North America, Europe and Asia
Host plants:
  Cloudberry and whortleberry
  (*Vaccinium*)
Conservation status:
  Not protected

Clossiana · Frigga

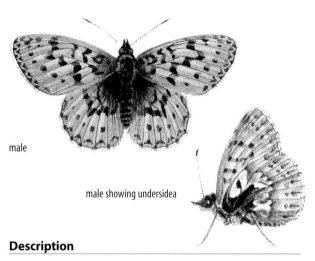

male

male showing undersidea

Description

This species always lives in moist habitats and is typically found in pine mires. Like Freija's Fritillary it has disappeared from much of its former range in southern Finland, probably due to changes in local microclimates induced by drainage. It is orange with zigzagging bands of black, and is also marked with curved bands of black dots and patches near the margins above. It is orange with a similar, but paler black, pattern and a few cream patches at the outer margin on the forewing. It is orange with large cream patches and a purplish tint on the hindwing below. The name of this butterfly is derived from that of Frigga, the wife of the Nordic god Odin. The caterpillar of this species is brown, mottled with black and the winter months are spent in the gray-brown chrysalis stage. The eggs are dull yellow and there is one brood from June to July.

Genus:
 Clossiana
Common names:
 Willow-bog Fritillary, Frigga's Fritillary
Size:
 32 to 46 mm (1¼ to 1¾ in.)
Male or female specimen:
 Male
Locality:
 North America and Europe
Host plants:
 Raspberry and willow
Conservation status:
 Not protected

Clossiana · Titania

male

male showing underside

Description

Titania's Fritillary is the biggest of the Clossiana genus and comes in two distinct forms. Just one of the many fritillaries to be found in Alpine meadows, and although it is very beautiful, it is also hard to identify. They do have a distinct row of triangles around the margins on the upperside. It is burnt orange with dull brown next to its body. There are also broken zigzagging bands of black, bands of black spots and patches, and then thin white bars along the outer margins above. The forewing is similar to the above, while the hindwing is red-brown with a yellow-white band below. In medieval folklore Titania was the queen of the fairies. Her namesake is a widespread species, well able to take advantage of localized conditions. The winter months are spent in the mottled brown caterpillar stage.

Genus:
 Clossiana
Common names:
 Titania's Fritillary, Purple Lesser Fritillary
Size:
 32 to 46 mm (1¼ to 1¾ in.)
Male or female specimen:
 Male
Locality:
 North America, Europe and Asia
Host plants:
 Willows and violets
Conservation status:
 Not protected

Coelites · Euptychioides

Description

Very little is known about the life cycle of this butterfly or which host plants the caterpillar feeds on. The main color of the *C. euptychioides* is light brown but there are amazing blue highlights on the trailing edge of the hindwing. The undersides are much lighter, but there is one distinctive feature in that there is a very large eyespot on the edge of the hindwing with three much smaller ones at the edge. It does not have the unusual wing shape of the *C. epiminthia*, which is the other species in the Coelitis genus. They inhabit the lowland rainforest area of Asia and Australia, where they fly in the dark of the forest understory.

Genus:
  Coelites
Common names:
  None
Size:
  80 mm (3⅛ in.)
Male or female specimen:
  Male
Locality:
  Malaysia, Australian region
Host plants:
  Not documented
Conservation status:
  Not protected

Coenonympha · Corinna

Description

This pretty butterfly is found in open grassy meadows up to a height of 3,000 ft. It is mostly seen in Corsica and Sardinia. From above it has a golden coloring, which is even brighter on the female is even brighter, while the underside is paler. It is associated with various grasses as larvae.

Genus:
  Coenonympha
Common names:
  Corsican Heath
Size:
  30mm (1⅛ in)
Male or female specimen:
  Male
Locality:
  Palearctic region
Host plants:
  Various grasses
Conservation status:
  Not protected

Coenonympha · Haydenii

Very little information has been documented about the life stages of this species. The caterpillar is green-brown with darker stripes.

male showing underside

Description

The adult Hayden's Ringlet has a bouncy flight and they can be seen in forest clearings, mountain meadows, and bog areas to 9,000 ft. (2,956 m). The upperside of the male is dark brown, while the female is much lighter. The underside of all wings have a narrow row of pale metallic scales at the margin and a pale terminal line. The hindwing has a submarginal row of five to seven black eyespots that are each ringed with orange. They have one brood from late June to early August. Although the Hayden's Ringlet is not a widespread butterfly, it can be plentiful across its range, which includes the Yellowstone and Grand Teton National Parks. This species was once commonly known as the Wyoming Ringlet.

Genus:
  Coenonympha
Common names:
  Hayden's Ringlet, Wyoming Ringlet, Yellowstone Ringlet
Size:
  48 mm (1⅞ in.)
Male or female specimen:
  Male
Locality:
  Southwest Montana, southeast Idaho and western Wyoming
Host plants:
  Various grasses
Conservation status:
  Not protected

Coenonympha · Hero

Description

The Scarce Heath Butterfly is a threatened species in Europe. Its total distribution ranges from the northeast of France, eastward through Russia, to Amur, Korea, and Japan. In Sweden, the species is classified as "near threatened" on the Swedish Red List. The exact reasons for its disappearance are unknown, but drainage and the planting of spruce are possibly the main reasons. Also the lack of grazing horses as in the "old" days may be an important factor. The *C. hero* is a uniform brown on the upperside, with a faint orange tint to the leading edge of the forewing. It also has a series of four orange spots around the margin of the hindwing. It has distinctive eyespots on the undersides of the hindwing, and to the inside is a thin line of white.

Genus:
  Coenonympha
Common names:
  Scarce Heath
Size:
  33 mm (1⅝ in.)
Male or female specimen:
  Male (underside)
Locality:
  Europe and Asia
Host plants:
  Various grasses such as *Lolium* and *Carex*
Conservation status:
  Extinct in certain areas of Denmark

Coenonympha · Inornata

male

male showing underside

chrysalis

The winter months are spent in the green-brown caterpillar stage.

Genus:
Coenonympha
Common names:
Prairie Ringlet
Size:
26 to 46 mm (1 to 1¾ in.)
Male or female specimen:
Male
Locality:
North America
Host plants:
Various grasses
Conservation status:
Not protected

Description

Prairie Ringlets can be found from May through September among wet prairies and blooming flowers. The wings on these butterflies range from dark orange-brown to pale cream, and the underside of the forewing usually has a small eyespot near its tip. The underside of the hindwing is gray-green with a wavy white median line. Prairie Ringlets, like other members of the *Satyridae*, characteristically hops when it flies. The larvae eat *Festuca* and *Agrostis* grasses. The Prairie Ringlet is successful in colonization because of its ability to exploit many types of grasses on host plants.

Cyllopsis · **Gemma**

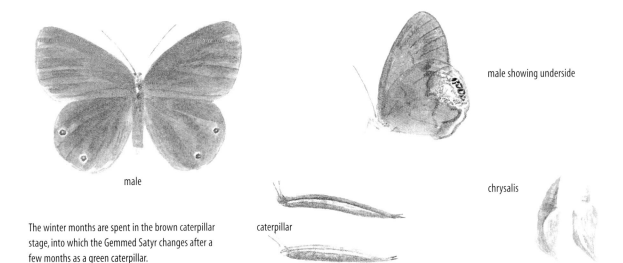

male showing underside

male

chrysalis

The winter months are spent in the brown caterpillar stage, into which the Gemmed Satyr changes after a few months as a green caterpillar.

caterpillar

Description

This butterfly lives near open, wet woodland, grassy areas near water, or near streams and ponds. The wings are brown and lack any eyespots. The underside of the hindwing has a silvery patch at the outer margin which contains four black reflective spots. Males patrol for receptive females, who lay their eggs on or near the host plant. Caterpillars feed at night and hide at the base of the plant during the day. There are several broods all through the year in south Texas; three broods from April to September elsewhere. Gemmed Satyrs from Texas and Mexico are redder than those from farther north and east. Although widespread in the sun belt, this species occurs locally and is rarely common. It has been suggested that the caterpillar's change in color, from green in summer to brown in the fall, allows it to blend with the seasonally changing colors of the grasses.

Genus:
Cyllopsis
Common names:
Gemmed Satyr
Size:
32 to 40 mm (1¼ to 1½ in.)
Male or female specimen:
Male
Locality:
Southeastern United States: the Atlantic Coast from Maryland south to central peninsular Florida; west to southeast Kansas, central Oklahoma, central Texas and northeastern Mexico
Host plants:
Various grasses, like Bermuda grass (*cynodon dactylon*)
Conservation status:
Not protected

Cyllopsis · Pyracmon

Description

The spring form of this butterfly looks different from the fall form and they were at one time considered separate species. Nabokov's Satyr is attracted to mud but not to flowers. They inhabit oak and pinyon woodland, and streamsides. The upperside is reddish brown, and the male forewing has dark scales in and below the cell. There are two small pairs of eyespots on the margin of the underside hindwing, and there is a little line which runs straight behind these eyespots. There are two broods from May to June and August to September.

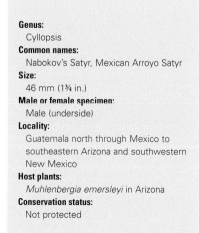

Genus:
Cyllopsis
Common names:
Nabokov's Satyr, Mexican Arroyo Satyr
Size:
46 mm (1¾ in.)
Male or female specimen:
Male (underside)
Locality:
Guatemala north through Mexico to southeastern Arizona and southwestern New Mexico
Host plants:
Muhlenbergia emersleyi in Arizona
Conservation status:
Not protected

Cymothoe · Sangaris

Description

The Sangaris Butterfly is nearly blood-red in color and is found in West Africa only at the edge of the rainforests. The underside of the wings are in sharp contrast to the upperside because they resemble the camouflage of dead leaves. The female is not as bright red as the male, and has rich red-orange in the middle of its wings. It has dark margins that are splashed with white, especially on the forewings, and zigzags on the hindwing. Very little has been documented about their life cycle or host plants.

Genus:
Cymothoe
Common names:
Red Glider, Blood Red Cymothoe
Size:
68 mm (2⅝ in.)
Male or female specimen:
Male
Locality:
West Africa
Host plants:
Not documented
Conservation status:
Not protected

Cynthia · Virginiensis

Description

The two large eyespots on the ventral hindwing distinguish this species from similar-appearing *C. cardui* and *C. annabella* which both have four spots. This butterfly appears to be most common during summer months, and it is known to fly throughout the year in Los Angeles County. It has a unique pattern on the underside of the hindwing, which apart from the two large eyespots shows a white-cream colored cobweb. It breeds principally on members of the daisy family, and some have been known to migrate to the Azores, southwestern Europe, Britain, and Hawaii.

Genus:
　Cynthia
Common names:
　American Painted Lady, Virginia Lady
Size:
　60 mm (2⅜ in.)
Male or female specimen:
　Male (underside)
Locality:
　North and South America, and Europe
Host plants:
　Gnaphalium spp. (cudweed or everlasting), *Antennaria* spp. (pussytoes), *Artemisia* spp. (sagebrush), *Anaphalis margaritacea*
Conservation status:
　Not protected

Cyrestis · Telamon

Description

This butterfly belongs to a genus of map-wing butterflies named after the fine lines that cross the forewings. The *C. telamon* differs from the *C. achates* and *C. maenalis*, in that it is not as dark in color and has a strong band of white across the wings and ends at the characteristic red-orange markings on the trailing edge of the hindwing. The edges of the wings are very dark with just a slight trace of white marks running around the periphery. These butterflies inhabit lowland rainforest areas.

Genus:
　Cyrestis
Common names:
　None
Size:
　50 mm (2 in.)
Male or female specimen:
　Male
Locality:
　Asia
Host plants:
　Possibly on *Tetracera sarmentosa* and *Ficus* species
Conservation status:
　Not protected

Danaus · Chrysippus Aegyptius

Description

Both sexes of the Plain Tiger Butterfly are similar. The male can be identified by the scent patches on the second vein of the hindwing. On the upperside, it appears as a large black patch toward the center of the wing, and on the underside, as a white centered black patch. The apical area on the underside of the forewing is a darker orange than the rest of the wing. It is a common butterfly of the arid, dry, and intermediate zones and is less commonly encountered in the wet zone. Its habitats include open spaces, fallow land, coastal dunes, scrub jungle, neglected coconut lands, and farmsteads. In fact, anywhere in which its principal larval foodplant, *Calotropis gigantea*, grows. Though never numerous, it is encountered all year round..

Genus:
  Danaus
Common names:
  Plain Tiger, African Monarch, Lesser Wanderer, Golden Danaid
Size:
  82 mm (3⅛ in.)
Male or female specimen:
  Female
Locality:
  African region
Host plants:
  Asclepias curassavica and *Calotropis gigantea*
Conservation status:
  Not protected

Danaus · Melanippus

Description

The Black-veined Tiger is a distant cousin of the famous American Monarch Butterfly (*Danaus plexippus*). The butterfly, with its bright colors, is distasteful to predators because of its poisonous host plants. It can usually be found near coastal or mangrove areas, and it is attracted to the dried plants of *Heliotropium indicum*. It has a leisurely flight, characteristic of the milkweed butterflies. It is likely that the Tiger butterflies are so named because of their orange color and black markings reminiscent of the big cat. The distinctive feature of this particular butterfly is the white ground of the hindwing which is traversed by black veins.

Genus:
  Danaus
Common names:
  Black-veined Tiger
Size:
  95 mm (3¾ in.)
Male or female specimen:
  Male
Locality:
  India to Sundaland and Sulawesi
Host plants:
  Milkweed and dogbane families, *Aclepiadaceae* and *Apocynaceae*
Conservation status:
  Not protected

Danaus · Plexippus

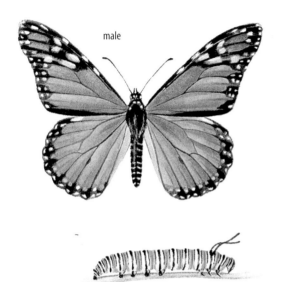

male

male showing underside

The caterpillar has bands in yellow, black and white with two black horns at the front and back.

Description

The Monarch Butterfly is renowned for its migration, traveling great distances to overwinter in a temperate climate. The upperside of the male is bright orange with wide black borders and black veins, while the hindwing has a patch of scent scales. The upperside of the female is orange-brown with wide black borders and blurred black veins. Both sexes have white spots on their borders and apex. They inhabit open areas including fields, meadows, weedy areas, marshes, and roadsides.

Adult Monarchs can be seen warming up by basking dorsally (with their wings open and toward the sun). Females lay eggs singly under the host leaves; and the caterpillars eat leaves and flowers. Most milkweeds, which are the host plant of the Monarch caterpillar, contain cardiac glycosides which are stored in the bodies of both the caterpillar and adult butterfly. These poisons are distasteful and emetic to birds and other vertebrate predators. After tasting a Monarch, a predator might associate the bright warning colors of the adult or caterpillar with an unpleasant meal, and avoid Monarchs in the future.

Adults make massive migrations from August to October, flying thousands of miles south to hibernate along the California coast and in central Mexico. A few overwinter along the Gulf coast or south Atlantic coast. Along the way, Monarchs stop to feed on flower nectar and to roost together at night. At the Mexico wintering sites, butterflies roost in trees and form huge aggregations that may have millions of individuals. During the winter the butterflies may take moisture and flower nectar during warm days. Most have mated before they leave for the North in the spring, and females lay eggs along the way. Residents of tropical areas do not migrate but appear to make altitude changes during the dry season.

Danaus

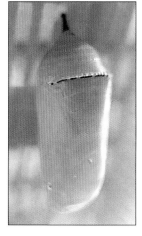

Shortly after emerging, the Monarch moves its wings up and down to dry them. It makes short flights until it is strong enough to fly a longer distance.

The Monarch caterpillar has eight pairs of legs, using five of them to hold its body up when it crawls, and the three remaining pair near its head to help the caterpillar crawl.

The Monarch chrysalis is one of the most beautiful objects in the natural world. It is jade and emerald green with glittering gold and black dots.

Genus:
  Danaus
Common names:
  Monarch
Size:
  100 mm (4 in.)
Male or female specimen:
  Male
Locality:
  Southern Canada south through all of the United States, Central America and most of South America. Also present in Australia, Hawaii and other Pacific Islands
Host plants:
  Milkweed
Conservation status:
  Not protected

Dione · Vanillae Insularis

Description

The Gulf Fritillary is a relatively large butterfly which can be seen in pastures, open fields, second-growth subtropical forest, and city gardens. Its upper wings are bright orange, and key marks include three silvery-white spots ringed in black on both of the upper front forewings. The underwings are brown with brilliant silvery spots. The caterpillars are orange with thick, purplish-gray stripes and long, black spines. Males patrol for females, who lay eggs on many parts of the host plant. The chrysalis is a mottled gray, resembling a dry, curled leaf as it hangs near the vine, often from the fence on which the vine is growing. The courtship behavior of the Gulf Fritillary is worth noting: males land in front of females and clap their wings repeatedly, close enough to catch the female's antennae between them. It is thought that this process releases chemicals that foster successful mating.

Genus:
  Dione
Common names:
  Gulf Fritillary
Size:
  74 mm (2⅞ in.)
Male or female specimen:
  Male
Locality:
  South America north through Central America, Mexico and the West Indies to the southern United States
Host plants:
  Various species of passion vine including maypops (*Passiflora incarnata*) and running pop (*P. foetida*)
Conservation status:
  Not protected

Dulcedo · Polita

Description

This is a genus with only one South American species which is quite remarkable because it has rounded, completely transparent wings. There is a very noticeable eyespot on the very edge of the hindwing, and a normally pale orange maplike line on the upper surfaces. The veins really stand out on the transparent, fragile wings, which are edged in black. It lives mainly in shady forests and breeds on various palms.

Genus:
 Dulcedo
Common names:
 None
Size:
 70 mm (2⅝ in.)
Male or female specimen:
 Female
Locality:
 South America
Host plants:
 Palms
Conservation status:
 Protected in some way

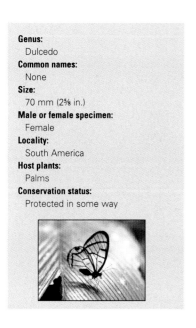

Elymnias · Agondas

Description

The genus Elymnias are medium- to large-sized and are very delicate and fragile butterflies. They are extremely rare, but the Common Palmfly is particularly abundant where plants of the species Palmae thrive. Its flight can be best described as a slow flapping and gliding motion. It tends to rest on leaves very often even after only a short flight. Due to its preference for shade, it is usually found flying under the cover of trees amongst the undergrowth. It has very distinct blue to purple submarginal spots on the forewing turning to purplish brown on the hindwing. Its underside is a rich brown filled with minute fasciae, turning lighter at the apex of the forewing.

Genus:
 Elymnias
Common names:
 Palmfly
Size:
 90 mm (3½ in.)
Male or female specimen:
 Male
Locality:
 Sri Lanka and India to Taiwan and
 Indochina, through Sundaland to the
 Lesser Sunda Islands and the
 Philippines
Host plants:
 Palmae
Conservation status: Not protected

Erebia · **Epipsodea**

male

Description

It is easy to identify this butterfly by its wing markings, which are dark brown. The upperside of both wings have white-centered submarginal eyespots in a yellow-orange patch. The underside of the forewing is similar to the upperside, and the hindwing is gray with submarginal black eyespots. Males patrol all day to watch for females, who lay their eggs on living and dead grasses. They have one brood from mid-June to early August. They inhabit moist open grassy fields, meadows, high prairies, and open forests. The Common Alpine is the most southerly of the Alpine butterflies, colonizing even at low altitudes. The caterpillar pupates in a sack of silk and grass in the spring, after spending the winter in hibernation.

Genus:
  Erebia
Common names:
  Common Alpine
Size:
  46 to 52 mm (1¾ to 2 in.)
Male or female specimen:
  Male
Locality:
  Alaska south through the Rocky Mountains to northern New Mexico; west across the prairie provinces to southwest Manitoba
Host plants:
  Grasses
Conservation status:
  Not protected

male showing underside

Erebia · **Fasciata**

male

Description

The male Banded Alpine is all black, the female is dark reddish-brown, and both are unmarked on the upperside. The underside has alternating broad bands of pale gray and brown cross wings which are more contrasting in the male. They inhabit wet tundra tussocks, boggy vegetation, lee sides of ridges, and gullies. When its wings are closed, displaying its distinctively banded underside, this species looks more like an Arctic (*Oeneis*) than any other alpine (*Erebia*). The bands break up the wing pattern, perhaps making the insect less readily apparent to predators. The actual tones of the bands and the reddishness of the upperside vary dramatically from place to place.

Genus:
  Erebia
Common names:
  Banded Alpine
Size:
  51 to 57 mm (2 to 2¼ in.)
Male or female specimen:
  Male
Locality:
  High Arctic Alaska north of treeline, east to Hudson Bay; also Asian High Arctic
Host plants:
  Grasses
Conservation status:
  Not protected

male showing underside

Erebia · Ligea

Description

This butterfly was named after the Isle of Arran, where they have reputedly been caught in the past, together with locations in Scotland, however no modern evidence exists of any colonies in Scotland. The Arran Brown has a delightful white band across its underwing, which makes it easy to identify. They prefer relatively low altitudes, and live on grassy slopes. The male is the more striking of the two sexes, with a rich orange band across the wings which contain relatively large pupiled eyespots on the forewing, and smaller ones on the hindwing. The female is much paler, but has much more pronounced eyespots. The pattern on the forewing is repeated on the underside, but the hindwing is much duller to act as a form of camouflage.

Genus:
   Erebia
Common names:
   Arran Brown
Size:
   57 mm (2¼ in.)
Male or female specimen:
   Male (underside)
Locality:
   Europe and Asia
Host plants:
   Grasses (*Poeceae*)
Conservation status:
   Not protected

Euphydryas · Phaeton

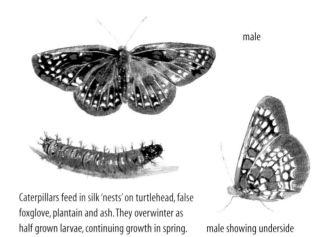

male

Caterpillars feed in silk 'nests' on turtlehead, false foxglove, plantain and ash. They overwinter as half grown larvae, continuing growth in spring.

male showing underside

Description

The Baltimore was named for George Calvert, the first Lord Baltimore. The coloring of the Baltimore matches the Calvert family crest. This lovely, little butterfly has black, orange bordered wings speckled with white and orange spots. Baltimores are found over much of the eastern United States, in varied habitats. In the Great Lakes they favor sphagnum bogs and wet meadows. The caterpillars of the Baltimore suffer high mortality from falling off the plant and from parasitism by wasps. Fourth-stage caterpillars hibernate in rolled leaves on the ground.

Genus:
   Euphydryas
Common names:
   Baltimore
Size:
   40 to 64 mm (1½ to 2½ in.)
Male or female specimen:
   Male
Locality:
   Very local. Nova Scotia west across the Great Lakes region to southeast Manitoba; south through the eastern United States to northern Georgia, northern Mississippi and northeast Oklahoma. Isolated records in northeast Texas and Nebraska
Host plants:
   Foxglove, ash and plantain
Conservation status:
   Not protected

Euploea · Alcathoe Eichhorni

Description

The Striped Black Crow has velvety brown wings above and the forewing is usually unmarked. The hindwing has a series of white submarginal spots and a corresponding row of whitish submarginal streaks. The dorsum of the forewing is curved in the male, but is straight in the female of this species.

This butterfly is often encountered feeding on flowering trees in the forest reserves in Singapore. At other times, they are rarely encountered, except singly, usually flying at treetop level. The species are distasteful to birds and is a model for some *Papilionidae* species and even some day-flying moths in Malaysia.

Genus:
Euploea
Common names:
Striped Black Crow
Size:
85 mm (3¼ in.)
Male or female specimen:
Male
Locality:
Asia and Australia
Host plants:
Asclepiadaceae, Apocynaceae, Moraceae
Conservation status:
Not protected

Euploea · Tulliolus Koxinga

Description

Deep rain forest clearings and paths at moderate heights are the favoured habitat of The Dwarf Crow from the Euploea genus. Its underside is a dull, brownish black and the female lacks the androconial patch. This butterfly is similar in appearance to The Common Crow butterfly. Both are distasteful and have evolved to mimic each other. .

Genus:
Euploea
Common names:
The Dwarf Crow
Size:
65mm (2⅝in)
Male or female specimen:
Male
Locality:
Oriental region
Host plants:
Moraceae (from the mulberry family) (CHECK
Conservation status:
Not protected

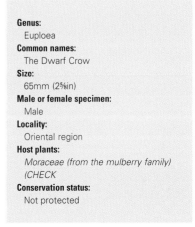

Euptoieta · Claudia

male

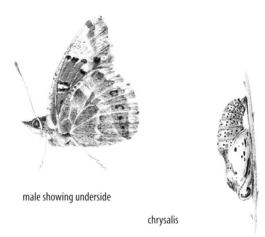

male showing underside

chrysalis

The caterpillar of the Variegated Fritillary includes more host plants in its diet than nearly any other North American species.

Genus:
Euptoieta

Common names:
Variegated Fritillary

Size:
40 to 64 mm (1½ to 2½ in.)

Male or female specimen:
Male

Locality:
Higher elevations of Argentina through Central America and Mexico to the southern United States; also Cuba and Jamaica. Regularly colonizes north through most of the United States except the Pacific Northwest

Host plants:
A variety of plants in several families including maypops (*Passiflora incarnata*), may apple (*Podophyllum peltata*), violets (*Viola*), purslane (*Portulaca*), stonecrop (*Sedum*) and moonseed (*Menispermum*)

Conservation status:
Not protected

Description

The Variegated Fritillary can be seen flying around in open sunny areas such as prairies, fields, pastures, road edges, and landfills. The upperside is tawny orange with thick dark veins and markings, with black spots near the margin. The hindwing margin is both angled and slightly scalloped. The underside of the hindwing has a mottled pattern and no silver spots. Males patrol short distances in flat, dry, open places. There are three broods from April to October in the North, four broods from February or March to November or December in the South. Adults feed from the nectar of a variety of plant species including butterflyweed, common milkweed, dogbane, peppermint, red clover, swamp milkweed, and tickseed sunflower.. This butterfly cannot tolerate extended periods of very cold weather and is usually found flying a couple of feet above grassland.

Eurodryas · Aurina

Description

The Marsh Fritillary is a beautiful butterfly that has suffered a rapid decline in England due to the loss and abandonment of flower-rich grassland. It is protected in many countries and is given protected status under the European Habitats Directive. It occurs in several different habitats, one being chalk downland and another is wet grassland. The female is larger than the male and has more rounded wings. The wonderful orange, yellow, and black pattern on the wings is repeated on the underside, which makes this a very colorful butterfly when stationary or in flight.

Genus:
Eurodryas
Common names:
Marsh Fritillary
Size:
46 mm (1¾ in.)
Male or female specimen:
Female
Locality:
Europe and Asia
Host plants:
Devil's Bit scabious (*Succisa Pratensis*), plantain (*Plantago*) species
Conservation status:
Protected in certain areas

Geitoneura · Acantha

Description

This is a medium-sized butterfly, with pale orange upper wings that have dark brown markings. There is one large eyespot on each wing. The underwing is similarly marked, but the orange is much paler and there are two conspicuous eyespots on the hindwing. They can generally be spotted in open country and grasslands. The female is significantly larger than the male, and has much more pronounced eyespots. Males will establish territories by perching on or near the ground in clear areas, waiting for newly emerged females.   When fertile females are chased by males, they signal to the males that they are fertile by settling on the ground and fluttering their wings. This signal makes the males quickly lose interest. These butterflies have an irregular flight, and prefer to settle on or near the ground.

Genus:
Geitoneura
Common names:
Eastern Ringed Xenica
Size:
52 mm (2 in.)
Male or female specimen:
Male
Locality:
Southern Queensland to Victoria and South Australia
Host plants:
Various grasses, including *Poa* species and the kangaroo grass (*Themeda australis*)
Conservation status:
Not protected

Hamadryas · Feronia Farinulenta

Description

This genus of butterflies is commonly called "calico butterflies" or "crackers." A mechanism on the wing allows them to make the characteristic clicking noise in flight which gives them their common name. This member of the species is quite dark with intense markings and a suffusion of pale blue. Another distinctive feature of the Blue Cracker is the lack of red rings around the eyespots on the hindwings.

Genus:
Hamadryas
Common names:
Blue Cracker, Cracker
Size:
72 mm (2¾ in.)
Male or female specimen:
Male
Locality:
North America
Host plants:
Member of the spurge family, (*Dalechampia*)
Conservation status:
Not protected

Heliconius · Aoede

Description

This genus is commonly called "longwings" due to the very elongated wings. Several of the heliconids have very similar patterns on their wings. On the *H. aoede* the yellow marks on the forewing are very well dispersed, and there are also bright red flashes on the forewings. The radiating lines on the hindwings continue right to the edge of the wing. It prefers open flowery spaces in the forest and waysides. The adults are gregarious and have communal roosting spots. The adults can live for anything up to nine months, because they collect amino acids from the pollen.

Genus:
Heliconius
Common names:
None
Size:
80 mm (3⅛ in.)
Male or female specimen:
Male
Locality:
South America
Host plants:
Passion flower family (*Passifloraceae*)
Conservation status:
Not protected

Heteronympha · Mirifica

Description

For many years it was thought the sexes were from different species, as the males tend to congregate toward the tops of hills and the females occur in the moist gullies below. They can be found at various sites around Sydney, from the coast to Katoomba. The wings of the adult male butterflies are brown with black markings. Each wing has an eyespot in the upper surface but not underneath. The females look entirely different, they are larger and black on top with gray underneath, and each forewing has a white bar and a white spot near the wingtip. There is also a small eyespot on the top of each hindwing. The caterpillars are initially green, later instars are brown with a darker dorsal line which narrows at each intersegment joint and widens on each segment. The tail has a forked projection, and a brown head that also has a pair of small horns, with pink tips..

Genus:
Heteronympha
Common names:
None
Size:
60 mm (2⅜ in.)
Male or female specimen:
Male (underside)
Locality:
Southern Queensland through New South Wales to Victoria
Host plants:
Various grasses
Conservation status:
Not protected

Hipparchia · Semele

Description

This is a beautifully cryptic species which always rests with its wings folded and the forewing held behind the hindwing. The underside of the hindwing is a mottled gray and brown. The underside of the forewing has a large light orange panel which contains two black eyespots with white pupils. The upperside of both wings, which are only shown in flight, are light brown with large pale orange bands. Females which are on average larger than males, are paler with lighter panels on the upperside. It can be found on dry, open habitats with sparse vegetation and much bare ground such as uncultivated grassland, heaths, sand dunes, and rocky slopes. Because of these requirements the species is mainly confined to coastal localities in much of northern and western Europe, including Ireland. Males take up position on a raised perch or bare ground and will investigate any flying insect. When unmated females are encountered, a courtship ensues. Much of the adult's time is spent basking in the sun. They alter their position and area exposed to the sun according to the air and body temperature.

Genus:
Hipparchia
Common names:
Grayling
Size:
50 mm (2 in.)
Male or female specimen:
Male
Locality:
Europe north to British Isles and southern Fennoscandia. Absent from most of SE Europe and Mediterranean islands. Also in temperate Asia.
Host plants:
Fine-leaved grasses such as Sheep's Fescue (*Festuca ovina*) and Red Fescue (*F. rubra*)
Conservation status:
Not protected

Hypolimnas · Misippus

Description

The upperside of the male is purple-black with a large white patch on each wing. The most common form of the female is orange, with a black apical area on the forewing divided by a band of white spots. The hindwing has a black marginal band. Males perch on or near the ground to watch for receptive females, and the caterpillars of this species live and feed communally. There are two broods from April to May and September to December. They inhabit tropical open, weedy areas. This butterfly is now resident on several of the Caribbean Islands, and may have been introduced by slave trading ships. Infrequently it wanders to Mississippi, Florida, and North Carolina.

Genus:
Hypolimnas
Common names:
Diadem Butterfly, Six-continent Butterfly, Danaid Eggfly
Size:
65 mm (2½ in.)
Male or female specimen:
Male
Locality:
Tropics and subtropics of Asia and Africa
Host plants:
Various plants in the mallow (*Malvaceae*), acanthus (*Acanthaceae*), morning glory (*Convolvulaceae*) and purslane (*Portulacaceae*) families
Conservation status:
Not protected

Hypolimnas · Salmacis

Description

This is an extremely variable butterfly which has a necklace pattern on its wings in a pretty blue-violet color. The pattern is even stronger on the hindwings than the forewings. The tips of the forewings are black with some white spots, which carry on along the margin of the hindwing. The female is slightly larger than her male companion, and may possibly be tinged with yellow. These butterflies favor open flowery areas and tend to breed on members of the purslane and nettle families.

Genus:
Hypolimnas
Common names:
Blue Diadem
Size:
100 mm (4 in.)
Male or female specimen:
Male
Locality:
Africa
Host plants:
Purslane and nettle familes, *Portulacaceae* and *Urticaceae*
Conservation status:
Not protected

Idea · D'urvillei

Junonia · Ceryne

Description

These very fragile butterflies inhabit the dense forests of Asia and the Australian region. They have a very weak flight and are quite easy to recognize. This species from New Guinea is different from the other *Ideas* in that it has a large area of irregular-shaped patches of black on the forewings. The majority of the hindwings and the rest of the forewings do not have the speckled pattern typical of the genus, but the margins do have the typical black and white markings. This is a typical rainforest species.

Description

The Marsh Commodore, as its name indicates, is common in damp areas and can be found throughout the entire year. The most notable feature of this specimen is the checkered margin all the way round the edges of the wings. On the inside of this is a band of bright orange, and then an area of very pale orange. The base of the wings is very dark, and there is a thin band of blue on the inside of the checkered areas.

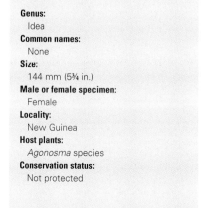

Genus:
  Idea
Common names:
  None
Size:
  144 mm (5¾ in.)
Male or female specimen:
  Female
Locality:
  New Guinea
Host plants:
  Agonosma species
Conservation status:
  Not protected

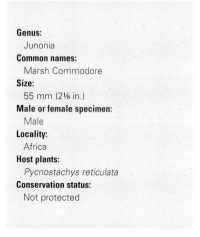

Genus:
  Junonia
Common names:
  Marsh Commodore
Size:
  55 mm (2⅛ in.)
Male or female specimen:
  Male
Locality:
  Africa
Host plants:
  Pycnostachys reticulata
Conservation status:
  Not protected

Junonia · Coenia

male

The caterpillar (below) of the Buckeye is black with broken white and red stripes along its sides and black, feathery spines. The chrysalis (left) has the colouring of soil sporadically laced with light snowfall. Caterpillars and adults overwinter but only in the South where it is warm.

Description

The Buckeye is a medium-sized butterfly with two large multicolored eyespots on its hindwings and one large eyespot on its forewings. The background color of the buckeye is mostly brown. Its forewing has two orange cell bars and one large eyespot inside the wide white area. The hindwing has two eyespots. The upper one is the largest and contains a magenta crescent. The two eyespots touch the light orange band at the bottom of the hindwings. The underside of the hindwing is brown or tan in the wet season (summer) and rose-red in the dry season (fall). Male Buckeyes perch during the day on low plants or bare ground to watch for females. They fly often to patrol their territory or to chase other flying insects. The Buckeye is often seen perching on protruding branches or resting on bare ground. Buckeyes prefer open, sunny areas with low vegetation and some bare ground.

Genus:
  Junonia
Common names:
  Buckeye
Size:
  50 to 64 mm (2 to 2½ in.)
Male or female specimen:
  Male
Locality:
  Southern United States and north along the coasts to central California and North Carolina, Bermuda, Cuba, Isle of Pines and southern Mexico
Host plants:
  Snapdragon (*Antirrhinum*) and toadflax (*Linaria*); the plantain family including plantains (*Plantago*); and the acanthus family including ruellia (*Ruellia nodiflora*)
Conservation status:
  Not protected

Kallima · Cymodoce

Description

The "dead leaf" butterflies (*Kallima* species) from Southeast Asia and East Africa get their common name from the uncanny resemblance of their wing undersides to dead plant leaves. So close is the mimicry, that the wing pattern appears to feature "moldy spots of decay," a "midrib" for the "leaves," and the tail touches the twig and appears like a leaf stalk. Less distinct dark lines run obliquely from the center line toward the wings' margins, mimicking the veins of a leaf. In contrast the uppersides are black with a bright blue base to the wings. The female is slightly larger with a larger orange band on the forewing apex. This butterfly can be seen all year round and lives in forested areas.

Genus:
  Kallima
Common names:
  Western Leaf Butterfly
Size:
  65 mm (2½ in.)
Male or female specimen:
  Male
Locality:
  Africa
Host plants:
  Various species of the shrubs and
  herbs in the family *Acanthaceae*
Conservation status:
  Not protected

Lasiommata · Petropolitana

Description

The *L. petropolitana* is the smallest of the wall browns. The male is a rather dull brown with a prominent eyespot on the apex of the forewing. Around the edge of the hindwings are smaller eyespots, which are a little more emphasized on the undersides. The female has eyespots in the same positions as the male, but they are much larger and are all set within an orange band. They prefer woodland glades in both lowland and upland settings, and tend to breed on common grasses.

Genus:
  Lasiommata
Common names:
  Northern Wall Brown
Size:
  42 mm (1⅝ in.)
Male or female specimen:
  Male
Locality:
  Europe and Asia
Host plants:
  Common grasses (*Festuca*
  species), *Gramineae*
Conservation status:
  Not protected

Lethe · Confusa

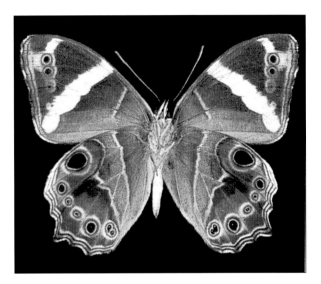

Description

Eyed Browns seldom stray from the wetlands where their caterpillars feed on sedges. They may be found even in very small sedge meadows. Their flights are from early July to early August. This species resembles *L. europa*, but it can be distinguished by the more defined eyespots on the underside of the hindwings. It also has a very distinctive broad, pale cream band on the underside of the forewings.

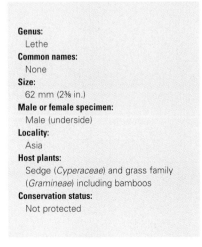

Genus:
  Lethe
Common names:
  None
Size:
  62 mm (2⅜ in.)
Male or female specimen:
  Male (underside)
Locality:
  Asia
Host plants:
  Sedge (*Cyperaceae*) and grass family (*Gramineae*) including bamboos
Conservation status:
  Not protected

Lexias · Cyanipardus

Description

This is a large butterfly whose basic color is black but with a lovely blue suffusion over the edge of the hindwings. The background color of the male is unbroken, while the female is speckled. Another way to identify this butterfly is the underside which has a noticeable green hue. These butterflies like to inhabit lowlands and their host plants have not been documented.

Genus:
  Lexias
Common names:
  None
Size:
  144 mm (5¾ in.)
Male or female specimen:
  Male (underside)
Locality:
  Asia
Host plants:
  Not documented
Conservation status:
  Not protected

Libytheana · Bachmanii

male showing underside

male

The winter is spent in the green chrysalis stage. The caterpillar is green with yellow stripes, with black tubercles on hump behind head.

Description

Snout butterflies get their name from their long mouthparts, which resemble an anteater snout. These butterflies have slightly orange-colored upper sides to their wings, with brown markings below. The larvae feed on hackberry and are usually kept in check by predators. When a drought reduces the numbers of these predators, the caterpillars mature rapidly in large numbers. The adults then emerge with a strong urge to migrate, and this can be quite spectacular as thousands of butterflies fly in tight groups across fields and roads. They look like small leaves blowing in the wind, an appropriate image for late summer to fall. The female is identifiable in this species by having six walking legs, whereas the males have only four otherwise they are similar in appearance . The genus Libytheana is composed of four species. They are to be found in the Western hemisphere in scrub habitats and desert washes. The Snout butterfly is strongly migratory.

Genus:
Libytheana
Common names:
Snout Butterfly
Size:
50 mm (2 in.)
Male or female specimen:
Male
Locality:
Great Lakes east to central New England, south through Rockies and East to Mexico
Host plants:
Hackberry
Conservation status:
Not protected

Limenitis · Reducta

Description

This butterfly flits along the edges of light woodland generally above head height and settles on the leaves of trees, shrubs, and bushes. The flight is quite rapid and so flat that it can be hard to follow. When the sun goes in the butterfly lowers its wings below its body and then raises them up more to bask when the sun reappears. A beautiful species which is generally encountered singly. It has a purple-blue sheen in strong light, but the undersides are very different, with bright orange, white, and brown. There is a single row of black spots around the margin of the hindwing, and a very distinctive white band.

Genus:
  Limenitis
Common names:
  South White Admiral
Size:
  54 mm (2⅛ in.)
Male or female specimen:
  Male (underside)
Locality:
  Europe
Host plants:
  Honeysuckle (*Lonicera* spp.)
Conservation status:
  Not protected

Marpesia · Eleuchea

Description

This group of butterflies is characterized by very long tails on the hindwings and carefully positioned eyespots. By viewing these butterflies from behind, the tails resemble antennae and the out-turned eyespots complete the illusion of eyes. A predator might be confused about the correct end of this butterfly to strike. These butterflies feed on Ficus and have elegant gliding flight. They can often be found in quite large numbers at their favorite mineral holes. This is a species of the West Indies, and is most common in the Greater Antilles.

Genus:
  Marpesia
Common names:
  Antillean Dagger Wing, Cuban Dagger Wing
Size:
  76 mm (3 in.)
Male or female specimen:
  Female
Locality:
  The West Indies. Strays very occasionally to the Florida Keys, probably from Cuba
Host plants:
  Fig trees (*Ficus*) in the family *Moraceae*
Conservation status:
  Not protected

Megisto · Cymela

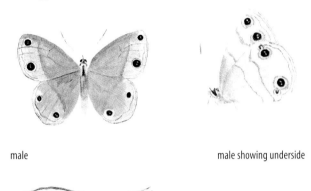

male   male showing underside

Megisto · Rubricata

Description

In the early morning and late afternoon, Little Wood Satyrs bask with their wings open while perched on tree leaves or on leaf litter. Adults have a slow bouncing flight and will rise as far as the tops of tall trees. Males patrol in the shade to find females. This butterfly has rounded wings with a uniform brown background color on the uppers. The forewing has two yellow-rimmed black eyespots both above and below, while the hindwing has two eyespots on the upperside. They prefer grassy woods and openings, old fields, especially in limey or basic soils. There is one brood from June to July in the North; two to three broods from March to September in the South.

Description

The Red Satyr is part of a genus of small brown butterflies that are very common where they occur, usually in grasslands, open fields and woodlands in canyons, They have rust colored postmedian lines on both wings. The female is duller in coloring.

Genus:
Megisto
Common names:
Little Wood Satyr
Size:
48 mm (1⅞ in.)
Male or female specimen:
Male
Locality:
Eastern Nebraska and northeastern Colorado south to eastern Texas; east through all of the eastern United States except northern New England, southern peninsular Florida and coastal Louisiana
Host plants:
Orchard grass (*Dactylis glomerata*) and centipede grass (*Eremochloa ophiuroides*)
Conservation status:
Not protected

Genus:
Megisto
Common names:
Red Satyr
Size:
50mm (2in)
Male or female specimen:
Male
Locality:
North and South America
Host plants:
Poaceae (grass family)
Conservation status:
Not protected

Melanargia · Galathea

Genus:
Melanargia
Common names:
Marbled White
Size:
52 mm (2 in.)
Male or female specimen:
Female
Locality:
Most of Europe (except Scandinavia) and North Africa and eastwards to Iran. It is stable in most European countries
Host plants:
Red Fescue (*Festuca rubra*) is thought to be essential in the diet of larvae but Sheep's-fescue (*F. ovina*), Yorkshire-fog (*Holcus lanatus*) and Tor-grass (*Brachypodium pinnatum*)
Conservation status:
Not protected

Description

The Marbled White is a distinctive and attractive black and white butterfly, unlikely to be mistaken for any other species. In July it flies in areas of unimproved grassland and can occur in large numbers on southern downland. It shows a marked preference for purple flowers such as Wild Marjoram, Field Scabious, thistles, and knapweeds. Adults may be found roosting halfway down tall grass stems. This species is widespread in southern Britain and has expanded northward and eastward over the last 20 years, despite some losses within its range. The larvae hatch from eggs which are dropped to the ground by the adult female and immediately hibernate for the winter.

Melanitis · Leda

Description

The Common Evening Brown is known to feed on padi. However, the foodplant is likely to be substituted with another monocotyledon (possibly bamboo) in Singapore, where padi is not grown.

The upperside of this butterfly is dark brown with a black subapical patch bearing two white spots and inwardly shaded with orange brown. The very variable underside is beige or grey, with fine dark brown striations. A submarginal row of yellow-ringed ocelli are usually found in the typical example. The variations in the undersides seem to be related to the wet and dry seasons in the region. The butterflies usually fly at dawn and shortly before dusk and are not normally seen during the day, except when disturbed.

Genus:
  Melanitis
Common names:
  Evening Brown, Common Evening Brown
Size:
  80 mm (3⅛ in.)
Male or female specimen:
  Female
Locality:
  Africa, Asia and Australian regions
Host plants:
  Padi, and possibly bamboo
Conservation status:
  Not protected

Melanitis · Zitenius Sumatranus

Description

M. zitenius sumatranus belongs to a genus of browns which can be found in Africa, Asia, and the Australian region. The forewing is curved, hooked, and indented, which is a characteristic of this genus. This is quite a large butterfly which has a very definite eyespot and a smudge on the forewing. It can be spotted flying around thickets between 1,800 and 3,300 ft. (550 and 1,000 m), and is known to occur in Sikkim, Malaya, and from Assam to Burma. It is thought that they breed on bamboo.

Genus:
  Melanitis
Common names:
  None
Size:
  90 mm (3½ in.)
Male or female specimen:
  Female
Locality:
  Asia
Host plants:
  Possibly bamboo
Conservation status:
  Not protected

Melinaea · Lilis Flavicans

Genus:	
Melinaea	
Common names:	
None	
Size:	
76 mm (3 in.)	
Male or female specimen:	
Female	
Locality:	
South America	
Host plants:	
Solanaceae spp.	
Conservation status:	
Not protected	

Description

This genus of butterflies is very similar in appearance to the *Heliconius*, but they have smaller compound eyes and androconial hairs between their wings. With the long wings and coloring of the heliconids, this genus is renowned for its mimicry. The basic color is a rich orange and can be either unmarked or filled with black lines. It favors open flower areas and likes to feed on the nectar from various flowers.

Right: Melinaea Lilis Messatis
Most often found in paths and clearings and in rain and tropical dry forests; disturbed habitats. Its underside is paler in color than its upperside. Female is similar.

Melitaea · Diamina

Description

This is one of the more distinctive of the smaller Fritillaries. Its upperside hindwing is extremely heavily marked, only a few small spots of orange ground color remain forming ghostly rows. The underside post discal spots are distinctive too, small black spots being present inside the arched black lunules. The female is slightly larger and less dark than the male. In contrast to the uppers, the underside markings on this species are very light with a prominent white band. They can be seen flying in grassy and flower meadows.

Genus:
  Melitaea
Common names:
  False Heath Fritillary
Size:
  42 mm (1⅝ in.)
Male or female specimen:
  Male (underside)
Locality:
  Europe and Asia
Host plants:
  Cow-wheat (*Melampyrum*, Plantain (*Plantago*)
Conservation status:
  Not protected

Mellicta · Britomartis

Description

The *M. britomartis* is a very good flier and is considerably spotted. The upperside has very dark markings, with rows of black marks crossing over the deep orange background. The underside is also a rich orange, with contrasting yellow bands crossing the wings. It lives and breeds in lowland meadows. There are around a dozen species within this genus that can be found in both Europe and Asia.

Genus:
  Mellicta
Common names:
  Assmann's Fritillary
Size:
  36 mm (1⅜ in.)
Male or female specimen:
  Male
Locality:
  Europe and Asia
Host plants:
  Plantago and *Veronica* species
Conservation status:
  Not protected

Memphis · Aureola

Description

The Memphis Aureola cam be found on the edges and paths of lowland rainforests at a height of up to 2,500 ft. Key characteristics include a mottled hindwing. The female is tailed and duller in color. The male can be rambunctious along trails.

Genus:
Memphis
Common names:
None
Size:
65mm (2⅝in)
Male or female specimen:
Male
Locality:
South America
Host plants:
Not known
Conservation status:
Not protected

Memphis · Proserpina

Description

This genus of butterflies is related to the *Anaea* family, and have very distinctive leaf-like undersides. The female *M. proserpina* is considerably larger than the male, with tails and a lot more green-blue metallic effect on the uppers. Also, another distinguishing feature of the female, is that its hindwing is much more angular than that of its mate. The undersides of both sexes differ very little, and they are easy to identify from their hatchet-shaped forewing. It can be seen flying in forested areas up to about 1,600 ft. (485 m), but as yet its caterpillar food-plants have not been discovered.

Genus:
Memphis
Common names:
None
Size:
74 mm (2⅞ in.)
Male or female specimen:
Male
Locality:
South America from Mexico to Costa Rica
Host plants:
Not found
Conservation status:
Not protected

Morpho · Rhetenor

Genus:
  Morpho
Common names:
  Blue Morpho
Size:
  140 mm (5½ in.)
Male or female specimen:
  Male
Locality:
  South and Central America
Host plants:
  Erythroxylum pilchrum
Conservation status:
  Not protected

Description

The Blue Morpho Butterfly is an iridescent blue butterfly that lives in rainforests of South and Central America, including Brazil, Costa Rica, and Venezuela. It is a species of neotropical butterfly that has brilliant blue wings (the females are not as brilliantly colored as the males and have a brown edge with white spots surrounding the iridescent blue area). The undersides (visible when the butterfly is resting) are brown with bronze-colored eyespots. Adults drink the juices of rotting fruit using their straw-like proboscis. The caterpillar of the Blue Morpho is red-brown with bright patches of lime-green on the back, and it eats the plant *Erythroxylum pilchrum* nocturnally (at night).

Neope · Pulaha

Description

speckled satyrids from Southeast Asia. It has the characteristic wing shape and speckled markings of the genus. The background color is black, but it is scattered with orange colored dots and specks, with the orange running along the veins of the forewing. The hindwing has a very slight scallop which almost gives the suggestion of a tail. It is usually seen flying around lowland and breeds on various grasses and bamboo.

Genus:
  Neope
Common names:
  None
Size:
  70 mm (2⅝ in.)
Male or female specimen:
  Male
Locality:
  Asia
Host plants:
  Grasses and bamboo
Conservation status:
  Not protected

Neorina · Hilda

Description

Neorina is a genus of butterflies which lives in the rainforests found from Sikkim to Java. Their characteristic feature is a very long antennae, which is about half the length of its forewing. The *N. krishna* is a big butterfly with very bold markings whose hindwing extends down into a proper tail. The background color is a warm brown, and a very distinctive yellow band cuts right across the forewing. It also has a large unpupiled eye at the apex.

Genus:
  Neorina
Common names:
  None
Size:
  93 mm (3½ in.)
Male or female specimen:
  Male
Locality:
  Java
Host plants:
  Unknown
Conservation status:
  Not protected

Neptis · Saclava

Description

The upperside of the Small Spotted sailor is blackish brown with a brown submarginal band. It favours open savannah and is easily distinguishable with its strong white banding. The Small Spotted Sailor is found in Africa, but other butterflies in the genus can be found in Australia, like the Neptis Shepherdi, Asia and Europe.

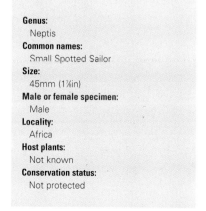

Genus:
  Neptis
Common names:
  Small Spotted Sailor
Size:
  45mm (1⅞in)
Male or female specimen:
  Male
Locality:
  Africa
Host plants:
  Not known
Conservation status:
  Not protected

Neptis · Shepherdi

Description

This family of butterflies is commonly called "gliders" or "sailors" because of the way in which they seem to glide through the air. *N. shepherdi* has the markings that are common throughout the genus, which is a black background dispersed with white lines and spots. However, the white marks on the forewing are more dispersed than say in *N. shepherdi latifasciata*, on which they are arranged in a band. There is also a broad white band across the hindwing.

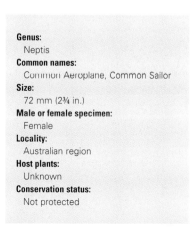

Genus:
  Neptis
Common names:
  Common Aeroplane, Common Sailor
Size:
  72 mm (2¾ in.)
Male or female specimen:
  Female
Locality:
  Australian region
Host plants:
  Unknown
Conservation status:
  Not protected

Nymphalis · Antiopa

male

The caterpillars of the Mourning Cloak are generally found in groups on deciduous trees and shrubs.

Genus:
  Nymphalis
Common names:
  Mourning Cloak, Camberwell Beauty
Size:
  65 mm (2½ in.)
Male or female specimen:
  Male
Locality:
  North America, Europe and Asia
Host plants:
  Chinese elm (*Ulmus* sp.). Willow (*Salix* spp.)
Conservation status:
  Not protected

Description

This is a medium-large butterfly, brown-black on its dorsal surface with wide yellow borders. A row of blue spots occurs adjacent to the yellow border. The males, like those of many other butterfly species, exhibit "territoriality." This means when they are disturbed, the butterfly will fly away, returning in a minute or two to the same place. The female lays her eggs in large clusters, and as the caterpillars remain in a group, they are fairly easy to find. This is one of America's most common butterflies and, although it is common in the suburbs, in the canyons it is usually limited to areas where its host plants grow. The Mourning Cloak can be seen during every month of the year. The species is multiple brooded and over-winters in the adult stage.

This butterfly is rare and much desired in England. It is known here by the common name of the 'Camberwell Beauty', and only occurs as a stray from mainland Europe. The above is a male showing its underside.

Nymphalis · Vau-album

male

Description

This is a large butterfly that can be found in upland deciduous or coniferous forests. The male Compton Tortoiseshell has deep golden-yellow markings on a rusty-brown wing. It has a single white spot and ragged wings which, when closed, resemble dead leaves or tree bark. It is between 2 and 3 in. (50 and 76 mm) in wingspan and likes being near the forests in the upper mountains. Their diet consists of rotting fruit and sap, and they also like to lick at mineral deposits. The caterpillar is pale green with yellow-green marks and black bristles or spines. The chrysalis is brown to green with fine lines and two projections on one end.

The "vau-album" of the scientific name refers to the whitish-silver "V" below, which places this butterfly close to the anglewings, although in every other respect it is clearly a tortoiseshell. It is occasionally numerous when conditions are right, clustering around fallen fruit, sap, or wet earth. But this big butterfly is notorious for its unpredictability; for years at a time it may be absent from a given district.

Genus:
Nymphalis

Common names:
Compton Tortoiseshell, Comma Tortoiseshell, False Comma

Size:
65 mm (2½ in.)

Male or female specimen:
Male

Locality:
Subarctic Alaska and Canada south to Oregon, Colorado, Minnesota and mountains of Missouri and North Carolina

Host plants:
Aspen and cottonwood (*Populus*), willows (*Salix*), gray birch (*Betula populifolia*), and paper birch (*B. papyrifera*)

Conservation status:
Not protected

Oeneis · Bore

male

male showing underside

The caterpillar is striped in shades of green brown, but very little additional information has been described about this species.

Genus:
Oeneis
Common names:
Arctic Greyling
Size:
50 mm (2 in.)
Male or female specimen:
Male
Locality:
In North America, high arctic tundra from Alaska east to Labrador
Host plants:
Grasses or sedges
Conservation status:
Not protected

Description

The wings of the Arctic Grayling are translucent, and the veins are usually white. The upperside is gray-brown with no eyespots, while the underside is light brown. The hindwing has a dark median band outlined in white. To find females, males perch and patrol all day on grassy hillsides or swales. Females lay eggs on dead grass or sedge blades. Two years are required to complete development—the first winter is passed by first-stage caterpillars, the second winter by mature caterpillars. There is only one brood in late July. The adult butterflies can be seen flying around the tundra, grassy alpine slopes, and subarctic bogs. Isolated populations have also been spotted in the alpine Rocky Mountains south to southwest Colorado and also on Mt. Albert, Quebec.

Oeneis · Chryxus

male

Description

The *C. arctic* inhabits open grassy, rocky, and woodland areas, meadows, and alpine tundra. The upperside is cream to brownish-orange. The forewing has one to four small black eyespots near the outer margin, and the hindwing has one to two. The forewing of the male has a dark patch of sex scales. The underside of the hindwing has black and white striations, a wide dark median band, veins with white scales, and only one black spot near the lower inner margin of the wing. They have one brood from late May to early June every year. It is possible that they are biennial because it is more numerous in even-numbered years in the Great Lakes region.

The caterpillar is greenish to brownish green, covered with reddish hair, and striped lengthwise along the body with a number of different colored stripes, including yellowish, white, and brownish. The yellowish head is striped with brown and it can reach a maximum length of 1¼ in. (32mm).

male showing underside

Genus:
  Oeneis
Common names:
  Chryxus Arctic
Size:
  50 mm (2 in.)
Male or female specimen:
  Male
Locality:
  Southern Alaska and Yukon Territory south through the western mountains to New Mexico; east across Canada to Manitoba
Host plants:
  Poverty oat-grass (*Danthonia spicata*)
Conservation status:
  Not protected

Oeneis · Nevadensis

Description

This butterfly inhabits coniferous forest openings, rocky hills, and meadow edges in the mountains. Its upperside is yellowish-tan with brown borders, the forewing has one or two eyespots, while the hindwing usually has one. The forewing of the male has a long patch of dark sex scales. The underside of the forewing is similar to the upperside, and the hindwing is mottled gray and brown with an indistinct median band. Males perch all day in valley glades and on hilltops to seek females. Eggs are laid on dry grasses. Caterpillars require two years to complete development, and pupation takes place at roots of grasses or under rocks. There is only one brood from May to July.

Genus:
  Oeneis
Common names:
  Great Arctic, Nevada Arctic, Pacific Arctic
Size:
  63 mm (2½ in.)
Male or female specimen:
  Male
Locality:
  Vancouver Island, British Columbia south in the Cascade Mountains and the Sierra Nevada to Tulare County, California; south along the coast to Sonoma County, California
Host plants:
  Grasses
Conservation status:
  Not protected

Pantoporia · Asura

Description

These variable butterflies can be found flying in forest clearings and along the edges in sunny situations. It is a dark brown (nearly black) color all over with a cream band which crosses both wings. There are also a number of cream marks on the forewing. The hindwing has quite a recognizable feature in a series of rectangular-shaped marks, almost like a diadem, each of which contains a single black dot. There are at least seven subspecies known and they can be found in Asia, Australia, Sri Lanka, and China.

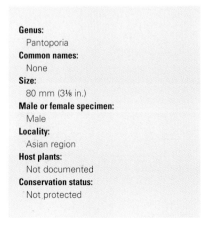

Genus:
　Pantoporia
Common names:
　None
Size:
　80 mm (3⅛ in.)
Male or female specimen:
　Male
Locality:
　Asian region
Host plants:
　Not documented
Conservation status:
　Not protected

Pareba · Vesta

Description

These butterflies come from a genus of very delicate-looking butterflies. They can most easily be identified by the shape of their elongated forewings. They are a very rich straw color in the background, with very few wing markings. They do however have a very pretty border of small orange marks within a small dark margin. Very little has been documented about this species.

Genus:
　Pareba
Common names:
　None
Size:
　60 mm (2⅜ in.)
Male or female specimen:
　Male
Locality:
　India to China
Host plants:
　Not documented
Conservation status:
　Not protected

Perisama · Chaseba Saussurei

Description

This is a complex genus of butterflies from South America, and unfortunately very little is known about the biology of *P. chaseba saussurei*. Its life history and also its larval foodplants are unknown, and they are rare and prized by collectors. The upperside in this species is quite a distinctive blue, while the undersides are rich orange on the hindwing and dark brown on the forewings with orange tips.

Genus:
  Perisama
Common names:
  None
Size:
  44 mm (1¾ in.)
Male or female specimen:
  Male (underside)
Locality:
  South America
Host plants:
  Bamboo, possibly *Chusquea* species
Conservation status:
  Not protected

Phyciodes • Mylitta

male

The caterpillars feed low down, near the ground, on thistle. The young caterpillars nibble away at the upper surface of the leaves and, with practice, it is possible to recognize these half-eaten leaves.

Description

The Mylitta Crescentspot butterfly is sexually dimorphic, and the specimen illustrated here is a male. In the female, the background color is not as uniform as on the male, some cells being dark orange, others a more pale yellow.

In the male the background color is orange above, with thin zigzagging bands of black curving around the front of the body and a submarginal band of scalloped orange patches with black dots in them on the hindwing. It is tan with black markings similar to above on the forewing, with large silver patches in bands across the hindwing below. Man's disturbance of the land throughout the West of America has spread thistles, and this has helped the Mylitta Crescentspot to expand its range. It prefers open areas such as meadows, forest clearings, grassland valleys, swamps, and fields; also along canals and streams. In far West, arctic-alpine meadows, and fell-fields.

Genus:
  Phyciodes
Common names:
  Thistle Crescent, Mylitta
  Crescentspot
Size:
  35 mm (1⅜ in.)
Male or female specimen:
  Male
Locality:
  North America
Host plants:
  Thistles
Conservation status:
  Not protected

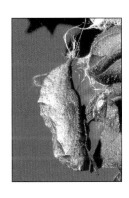

The chrysalis of the Mylitta Crescentspot is light mottled brown with small bumps.

Pierella · Rhea

Description

The most distinguishable feature of this South American butterfly is the shape of the wings. The forewings are elongated in contrast to the hindwings. The two pairs of wings are also quite different in color. The forewing has a brown background, while the hindwings are more of a purple-black. Around the margins of the hindwings are a row of black-ringed white-pupilled eyespots. This particular butterfly flies in various countries within the Amazon rainforest.

Genus:
Pierella
Common names:
None
Size:
74 mm (2⅞ in.)
Male or female specimen:
Male
Locality:
South America, Brazil, Amazon basin
Host plants:
Heliconia possibly
Conservation status:
Not protected

Polygonia · c-album

Description

The Comma butterfly is common to the United Kingdom, but can be found right across Europe through to Asia and Morocco. The white marking on its underwing is said to resemble a Comma, hence the name, and it has a distinctive ragged profile, designed to mimic a fallen leaf. Their caterpillars, meanwhile, cunningly resemble a bird dropping. The early 19th century saw a dramatic decline in the number of Comma sitings, but the population has built back up again and it is spotted regularly across Britain.

Genus:
Polygonia
Common names:
Comma
Size:
50mm (2 in)
Male or female specimen:
Male
Locality:
Eurasia
Host plants:
Urticaceae (nettles) and *Salix (willow)*
Conservation status:
Not protected

Polygonia · Interrogationis

male

The caterpillar is beige to rust-coloured and when mature bears a pair of black, branched spines on its head and several on each segment.

male showing underside

Description

The forewings of the Question Mark butterfly are hooked, and the upperside of the wings are red-orange with black spots. The color of the top of the hindwing changes depending on the time of year. In the summer, it is mostly black with a short tail, the winter form has a lot of orange and a longer, violet-tipped tail. The underside is light brown; the hindwings have a pearly-white question mark in the center, giving the butterfly its name. Adult males will sit during the afternoon hours on tree trunks or leaves waiting for females. They will, however, leave their perches to chase other insects and even birds. The female will lay eggs alone, or stacked, on the leaves of plants, which are not always the caterpillar's host plants. When the caterpillars appear, they must find a host plant to feed on. Some adults will stay in the northern United States to hibernate, while others will migrate south.

Genus:
Polygonia
Common names:
Question Mark
Size:
62 mm (2⅜ in.)
Male or female specimen:
Male
Locality:
East of Rockies from Saskatchewan to Texas and Mexico and east to Maritimes and Florida
Host plants:
Nettles, hackberries, and hops
Conservation status:
Not protected

Polygonia · Progne

male

The caterpillars vary in colour: tan or rust, marbled with dull green and bearing short, branched spines along back and on head.

Chrysalis tan to brown with dark streaks.

Description

These butterflies can be found along dirt roads, along streamsides, and within clearings in rich deciduous or coniferous woods, in aspen parks, yards, and gardens. Often in hilly terrain or canyons. The wing margins of the Gray Comma are ragged and this butterfly has two seasonal forms. In fall and spring they are tawny-orange above with yellow-spotted dark borders and relatively little black spotting. Summer butterflies have very dark chocolate-brown hindwings, above, with tawny-base, yellow spots, and heavier black spotting. The undersides are gray-brown and more uniform, but heavily striated in summer. There is a silver L-shaped comma on the hindwing, and one arm is shorter in the summer form; both arms tapering to points. There are two flights in April and May, when the winter form emerges from hibernation, mates, and lays eggs which develop into the summer generation. Summer adults fly from June to August, laying eggs of the winter generation which appear in October and then hibernates.

Genus:
Polygonia
Common names:
Grey Comma, Dark-grey Comma, Dark-grey Anglewing
Size:
48 mm (1⅞ in.)
Male or female specimen:
Male
Locality:
British Columbia, Wyoming and Kansas east to Nova Scotia, Missouri and North Carolina; possibly Alaska
Host plants:
Currants, gooseberries, and azalea
Conservation status:
Not protected

male showing undersides

Polygonia · Satyrus

male

Genus:
  Polygonia
Common names:
  Satyr Anglewing
Size:
  50 mm (2 in.)
Male or female specimen:
  Male
Locality:
  British Columbia to Newfoundland
  in S. Canada; in U.S. from the
  Pacific to eastern edge of Rockies,
  south to Mexico
Host plants:
  Primarily *Urtica* spp., but also
  Humulus spp. and perhaps *Betula*
Conservation status:
  Not protected

DESCRIPTION

Satyr Anglewings are able to emerge and survive long before other butterflies have emerged from hibernation and while others are still on their migration grounds to the South. In early spring, look for Satyr Anglewings in bushy open areas, especially around low spots on pathways where mountain bikers have churned the soft public trails into impassable little mud baths.

Its wing margins are ragged, and the uppersides are a bright tawny-golden with black blotches. The hindwings lack strong dark margins, having only a band of golden spots narrowly lined with brown. Beneath, the male is bright yellow-tan marked with tiny dots and striations, while the female is brown, slightly violet-tinged, darker on the basal half. They also have a silver comma mark in the hindwing below, which is clubbed or hooked.

male showng underside

Chrysalis is tan, angled and hangs from tree trunks or stones. For protection the caterpillar wraps the leaf it is feeding upon loosely around itself.

Polyura · Athamus

Description

This tropical Asiatic butterfly is a strong, fast flier fond of overripe fruit. The word *nawab* invokes the image of an Indian ruler seated on a beautiful silken rug, which was the inspiration for the common name. The rather small butterflies prefer to live in forests, but have adapted to other living spaces when needed. The species can be distinguished from other tropical butterflies by the pale yellow-green bands that are topped by a single spot on both sides of its brown wings and the paired tails on each of its hindwings. A Common Nawab butterfly takes approximately three months to complete metamorphosis.

Genus:
Polyura
Common names:
Common Nawab
Size:
80 mm (3⅛ in.)
Male or female specimen:
Male
Locality:
India and Southeastern Asia, including the islands of Hong Kong, the Malay Archipelago and the Philippines
Host plants:
Albizzia, Acacia and Poinciana
Conservation status:
Not protected

Prepona · Demophon

Description

This beautiful butterfly ranges from Mexico to South America and thrives in the warm shelter of the rainforests. Unfortunately, much of its habitat is being destroyed. The upper sides of their wings resemble black velvet paintings, iridescent metallic green-blue or blue-purple patterns on a rich black background. The intricate silver-brown, leaf-like underwing patterns, which serve as camouflage, are the best way to distinguish this species. In flight, Banded King Shoemakers may appear more similar to birds in a flock, than butterflies, having a very strong swift flight. They have a smell very similar to vanilla.

Genus:
Prepona
Common names:
Banded King Shoemaker, Silver King Shoemaker
Size:
140 mm (5½ in.)
Male or female specimen:
Male
Locality:
Mexico to South America
Host plants:
Leguminosae
Conservation status:
Not protected

Pyronia · Tithonus

Description

To be found generally from mid-July to early September, this butterfly is very common in southern England with it becoming a rarity as one travels north. The Gatekeeper is golden brown in appearance with the upper wings having a wide dark brown border enclosing a lighter golden brown/orange patch. Both sexes have a large black eyespot usually containing two white pupils near the tip on the forewing. The male has a broad band of dark scales known as the sex band present on each forewing. Also present is one small white dot on the upper hindwing although several may be present. The underside hindwing is mottled brown with a beige band and a row of white dots. The forewing is a paler version of the upper side.

Genus:
Pyronia
Common names:
Gatekeeper, Hedge Brown
Size:
38 mm (1½ in.)
Male or female specimen:
Male
Locality:
Europe and Asia
Host plants:
A wide range of fine and medium bladed grasses including: couch (*Agropyron repens*), various bents (*Agrostis* spp.), fesques (*Festuca* spp.) and meadow grasses (*Poa* spp.)
Conservation status:
Not protected

Salamis · Parhassus

Description

S. parhassus is the largest species in this genus which is confined to the African region. It is one of the most vibrant of all the Congo butterflies with fancy leaflike edges and intense coloring. It has a pearly green background with a contrasting black hooked tip to its forewing. There are a series of dark spots on both sets of wings, along with a set of black spots around the edges. The undersides are also pearly with eight very distinct red spots. It inhabits forests, woodland, and scrub land throughout most of Africa. The caterpillar lives off *Asystasia* which is a member of the acanthus family.

Genus:
Salamis
Common names:
Mother of Pearl
Size:
90 mm (3½ in.)
Male or female specimen:
Female
Locality:
African region
Host plants:
Asystasia
Conservation status:
Not protected

Sallya · Boisduvali

Description

This specimen comes from a genus of African butterflies otherwise known as tree nymphs. They like woodland, scrub, and secondary forest which has developed where primary forest has been cleared. In the *S. boisduvali* the uppers are a soft brown color with a dark area around the outer edges of the hindwing. On the inside of the dark margin is a row of small black dots. On the leading edge of the forewing there are two black bands. Although the two sexes are similar, the female does tend to have darker markings. These butterflies have been spotted in large numbers in the region of Ethiopia.

Genus:
Sallya
Common names:
Brown Tree nymph
Size:
55 mm (2⅛ in.)
Male or female specimen:
Male (underside)
Locality:
African region
Host plants:
Excoecaria
Conservation status:
Not protected

Speyeria · Diana

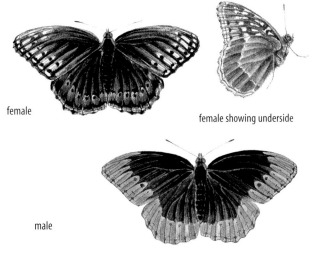

female

female showing underside

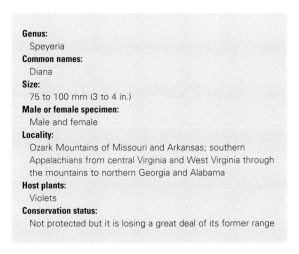

male

Description

These large butterflies inhabit fields, edges, and openings in moist, rich, forested mountains and valleys. The adults feed on dung and flower nectar from plants including common and swamp milkweeds, ironweed, red clover, and butterflybush. The upperside of the male wings is black at base, and orange at outer portions. In contrast the female is black with blue on the outer part of the hindwing. The undersides lack the typical *Speyeria* spot pattern. Males patrol for females in deep woods. Females walk along the ground laying single eggs on dead twigs and leaves near violets. The caterpillars hatch and overwinter without feeding. In the spring they feed on leaves and flowers of violets. There is one flight from mid-June to early September.

Genus:
Speyeria
Common names:
Diana
Size:
75 to 100 mm (3 to 4 in.)
Male or female specimen:
Male and female
Locality:
Ozark Mountains of Missouri and Arkansas; southern Appalachians from central Virginia and West Virginia through the mountains to northern Georgia and Alabama
Host plants:
Violets
Conservation status:
Not protected but it is losing a great deal of its former range

Speyeria · Idalia

male

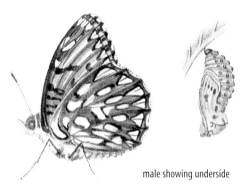

male showing underside

The chrysalis is light brown, and there is only one brood each year.

Description

The Regal Fritillary is one of the most striking butterflies to be found on the prairie. As a large orange and black butterfly, it may be confused with the Monarch if seen from a distance. However, the hindwings are quite different —dark above and covered with large off-white spots below. Observed closely, the forewings are distinctive also. The short dark lines running crosswise to the wing veins are not seen on Monarchs. Females have a dark patch at the wing tip and a row of small white spots along the outer margin. On the upper hindwings the spots are all pale yellow on females. On males, the inner row is white and the outer row is orange. The caterpillars, as is true of most fritillaries, eat only violets. In particular, Regals prefer the Birdsfoot Violet (*Viola pedata*) and Prairie Violet (*Viola pedatifida*). The newly hatched caterpillars overwinter and begin eating the following spring. They are black and yellow with short branching spiny hairs.

Genus:
  Speyeria
Common names:
  Regal Fritillary
Size:
  72 to 94 mm (2¾ to 3¾ in.)
Male or female specimen:
  Male
Locality:
  Southern Wisconsin west to Montana and south to northeast Oklahoma
Host plants:
  Violets
Conservation status:
  Not protected but they have gone into sharp decline due to agriculture destroying their natural habitat

The Speyeria Nokomis is also known as the Nokomis Firtillary or Western Seep Fritillary. Its upperside is a red/orange color with dark markings. The female is brown with either yellow or pale blue submarginal and discal markings.

Speyeria · Zerene

male

Description

The Zerene Fritillary inhabits conifer forests, sagebrush, coastal meadows, and dunes. Males patrol all day seeking females. Females may delay egg-laying until late summer. Eggs are laid on leaf litter near violets; unfed first-stage caterpillars overwinter on a silken mat. In the spring, caterpillars feed on the leaves of violets. The upperside of the Zerene Fritillary is bright to dull orange with heavy black markings. The base of the forewing underside is usually flushed with reddish orange; the ground color of the hindwing underside is dark reddish brown. The outer edge of the forewings is very slightly concave. This is a highly variable species and it can be confused with several other species. The Zerene Fritillary is one of three similar species (*S. zerene, S. egleis,* and *S. coronis*) in which the silver spots on the margin of the hindwing underside are low and rounded, usually oval or lens-shaped in outline. In most other fritillaries in the west these spots are higher and more triangular.

Genus:
  Speyeria
Common names:
  Zerene
Size:
  44 to 64 mm (1¾ to 2½ in.)
Male or female specimen:
  Male and female
Locality:
  Coastal British Columbia south and east to Montana, south to central California, Arizona and New Mexico
Host plants:
  Violets including *Viola adunca, V. lobata, V. cuneata, V. nuttallii* and *V. purpurea*
Conservation status:
  Not protected

female showing underside

Stibochiona · Nicea

Description

This is a fairly common rainforest butterfly found at moderate elevations. The upper surface of the wings of the male is velvet black and the female dark green. In both sexes, the upper surface of the forewing has rows of white spots on the wing margin and toward the inner area with obscure dull blue lines between them. There are also one or two white spots present on the middle area. The hindwing has a prominent row of black spots inwardly blue bordered (green bordered in female) and outwardly white. This butterfly is a rapid flier but settles frequently with wings open.

Genus:
  Stibochiona
Common names:
  None
Size:
  70 mm (2⅝ in.)
Male or female specimen:
  Male
Locality:
  North India to south China and the Malay Peninsula
Host plants:
  Not documented
Conservation status:
  Not protected

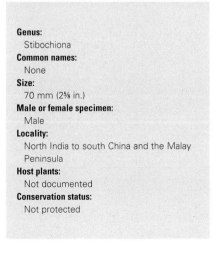

Stichopthalama · Louisa

Description

This butterfly is quite easy to identify from its bright orange suffusion on the inner two-thirds of its uppers. It also has a band of black marks that look like arrows, around the outer margins of the wings. In comparison the undersides are very pale with the inner areas very slightly darker, and marked with thin lines. There are two quite distinctive eyespots on each of the hindwings. The antennae of this genus tend to broaden toward the tip, rather than the normal club shape. They live in the rainforest and breed on various types of grasses, including bamboo.

Genus:
Stichopthalama
Common names:
None
Size:
140 mm (5½ in.)
Male or female specimen:
Male
Locality:
India to Burma
Host plants:
Grasses including bamboo
Conservation status:
Not protected

Tanaecia · Lepidea

Description

T. lepidea comes from a large genus of Asian butterflies which are found in the rainforests of India to the Philippines. It has quite distinctive two-tone markings on its uppers, mostly dark brown, but the edges of the hindwings fade to a pale beige or cream. The shape of the forewing is both hooked and curved. The undersides of this species are a much lighter brown. There are thought to be around six subspecies and they can be found on hilly country at around 2,500 ft. (760 m).

Genus:
Tanaecia
Common names:
Gray Count
Size:
70 mm (2⅝ in.)
Male or female specimen:
Male
Locality:
Asian region
Host plants:
Melastoma malbathricum and *Careya arborea*
Conservation status:
Not protected

Taygetis · **Albinotata**

Description

This butterfly comes from a genus of around 27 species of browns which frequent Central and South America. This is quite a large brown with a very neat row of large white spots on the hindwings. The cream markings around the edges of the wings give the appearance that they are scalloped. The undersides are light and dark brown and have two cream bands crossing the wings. As yet their caterpillar foodplants have not been ascertained, but it is most likely that they feed off certain types of grasses.

The 30 species of large brown butterflies in this genus have distinctive hindwing margins and are associated with mesic tropical and humid rain forests.

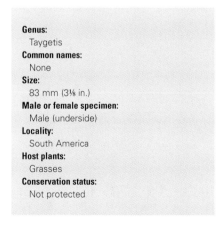

Genus:
   Taygetis
Common names:
   None
Size:
   83 mm (3⅛ in.)
Male or female specimen:
   Male (underside)
Locality:
   South America
Host plants:
   Grasses
Conservation status:
   Not protected

Tisiphone · Abeona

Vanessa · Atlanta

(male) The Red Admiral tends to be slow to take flight and not at all fearful of humans.

male showing underside

Caterpillars are bristly and dark with a pale yellow stripe running down each side.

Description

The Sword Grass Brown is a beautiful, but slow-flying butterfly. It's from an Australian genus of particularly large butterflies, all of which have distinctive markings. The Grass Brown's upperside is dark brown with a narrow orange band surrounding a single ocellus, as with the female of the species. It is often found in rocky meadow areas.

Red Admirals have dark black-brown wings, each with an orange-red band. The forewing tips are black with white spots; the underside is orange, blue, and white, while the hindwings are camouflaged dark brown. After hibernation, adults have a strong urge to fly northward, bringing immigrants from the continent throughout the summer. By mid-August they start to return south, leading to a build up in southern England in fall. During the summer females lay single eggs on the growing tips of nettles. After a week or so, the caterpillars hatch and each spins a tent around itself by fastening a young leaf double with silk. Four weeks later caterpillars pupate in a similar "tent." Adults may hibernate in England, usually choosing an exposed site such as a tree trunk, and many perish. They cannot survive the coldest winters; most of North America must be recolonized each spring by southern migrants.

Genus:
Tisiphone
Common names:
Sword Grass Brown
Size:
70mm (2 ⅞in)
Male or female specimen:
Female
Locality:
Australia
Host plants:
Arbutus
Conservation status:
Not protected

Vanessa · Virginiensis

male

male showing
undersides

Description

These butterflies can be seen frequently in open places with low vegetation including dunes, meadows, parks, vacant lots, and forest edges. The American Painted Lady is a true Brush-foot butterfly. It has two blue dots divided by two black dots on the hindwing. On the forewing there are four white dots at the wing tips, the middle two of which are higher and smaller than the outer ones. Below these is a long tear-shaped spot.

They are found year-round throughout Florida in open fields and gardens. They feed on mud and the nectar of many plants. The cobweb pattern and large blue eyespots on the undersides of the wings are unique identifiers. The pale yellowish green eggs are laid individually on the upperside of leaves. The caterpillars are black with bands of yellow and black lines. In between the bands are orange or red spots at the base of black branching spines. They create silk nests with leaves, and the chrysalis, which is brown with gold spots, is often formed in the nest.

Genus:
Vanessa
Common names:
American Painted Lady
Size:
56 mm (2¼ in.)
Male or female specimen:
Male
Locality:
Southern United States, Mexico and Central America south to Colombia. Migrates to and temporarily colonizes the northern United States, southern Canada, the West Indies and Europe
Host plants:
Plants in the sunflower family: sweet everlasting (*Gnaphalium obtusifolium*), pearly everlasting (*Anaphalis margaritacea*), plantain-leaved pussy toes (*Antennaria plantaginifolia*), wormwood (*Artemisia*), ironweed (*Vernonia*) and burdock (*Arctium*)
Conservation status:
Not protected

Vindula · Erota

Description

This is a large tailed Nymphalid, which has the habit of continuously opening and closing its wings as it feeds on nectar. The males are a bright orange above and below, while the females are a beautiful pale sky blue above and straw colored below. The dry season and wet season forms of this butterfly show marked variation in both size and intensity of color, and the width of the bands. The males are much smaller than the females. It is an uncommon butterfly found in the intermediate and wet zones of the island wherever suitable forest cover exists. It rarely visits home gardens or cultivated areas, unless they are in very close proximity to a forest. The females are quite scarce and retiring.

The Vindula Arsinoe Andea is also more commonly known as Cruiser. Its favoured habitat is rainforest clearings and paths and secondary vegetation. They are often observed at mud puddles or sap flows. The female's ground colour is tan and its markings are heavier with extra eyespots.

Genus:
Vindula
Common names:
Cruiser
Size:
95 mm (3¾ in.)
Male or female specimen:
Male
Locality:
Southeast Asia, Australia, South Pacific islands of Oceania
Host plants:
Passifloraceae
Conservation status:
Not protected

Family
Lycaenidae

This is a family of small, usually brilliantly colored butterflies, which include the Hairstreaks, Blues, Coppers, and Metalmarks, and are some of the most beautiful butterflies in the world. These slender butterflies have wonderful iridescent upper surfaces to their wings, which are usually metallic blue, green, or copper. There are over 5,000 species in this family. Two distinctive characteristics are that their antennae are ringed with black and white, and the fact that the anterior legs in males may be shorter. Lycaenids are often gregarious and breed principally on members of the pea family or Leguminosae. The butterfly below is the Jamaican Green Hairstreak (*Cyanophrys crethona*) which is the largest member of this family found in the West Indies.

Abisara · Savitri

Description

This is a forest butterfly and is rather timid. It shares the habit of flitting from perch to perch and settling with half-open wings. The species is rarely seen and usually observed in shaded areas along paths within the nature reserves of Singapore. The butterfly is a beige brown with a slight hint of lilac in some light, and possesses a pair of white transverse stripes on the forewing. It has black submarginal spots along the hindwing, and has a pair of white-tipped tails, several millimeters long. There are two pairs of eyespots on the hindwings, each pair a different size.

Genus:
  Abisara
Common names:
  None
Size:
  54 mm (2⅛ in.)
Male or female specimen:
  Male
Locality:
  Asian region
Host plants:
  Mysinaceae
Conservation status:
  Not protected

Agriades · Aquilo

Description

This is a small butterfly, whose appearance varies considerably depending on its location. The upperside of males is typically grayish to greenish-blue, and appears iridescent. The forewing is bordered with black along the side, and there is a single black spot near the center. The hindwing may have a row of small black dots along the edge. Females are orangish-brown on the upperside, possibly with patches of pale blue, and are marked similarly to males. Underneath, both sexes are grayish brown. The underside of the forewing is marked with white spots, possibly with tiny black centers; the hindwing may be spotted with white, black, or both. Generally, this species is found throughout the temperate regions of the Northern Hemisphere.

Genus:
  Agriades
Common names:
  Arctic Blue
Size:
  22 mm (⅞ in.)
Male or female specimen:
  Male
Locality:
  Europe and Asia
Host plants:
  Saxifraga aizoides, Saxifraga oppositifolia
Conservation status:
  Not protected

Agrodiaetus · Damon

Description

The two sexes of Damon's Blue are very differing on their uppersides. The male is mostly a turquoise-blue which has a darker margin around all the wings. The female is quite a plain brown, but both the sexes have a white fringe. On the undersides there is a quite distinctive white band across the beige hindwing. This butterfly likes open, flowery meadows and breeds on Onobrychis viciifolia (Leguminosae).

Genus:
  Agrodiaetus
Common names:
  Damon's Blue
Size:
  32 mm (1¼ in.)
Male or female specimen:
  Male (underside)
Locality:
  Europe
Host plants:
  Onobrychis viciifolia
Conservation status:
  Not protected

Ancyluris · Formosissima Venabalis

Description

There are around 20 species with the genus *Ancyluris*, all of which have elongated forewings and extended hindwings which end in short or truncated tails. In the *A. formosissima venabalis* the undersides are a beautiful array of colors, with bold markings of metallic greenish-turquoise on the forewing. It is white on the base, and red and black on the hindwing. The uppers are a repeat of the undersides but less vibrant in color, and a row of green spots on the margin of the hindwing. Little is known about the life cycle of this butterfly, but it is known to inhabit the rainforests of Ecuador and Peru.

Genus:
  Ancyluris
Common names:
  None
Size:
  44 mm (1¾ in.)
Male or female specimen:
  Male (underside)
Locality:
  Ecuador and Peru
Host plants:
  Not documented
Conservation status:
  Not protected

Apodemia · Mormo

Description

The common name, Metalmark, relates to the presence of metallic colored markings on the wings in many species in the family. However, the Morman Metalmark lacks these metallic markings. The females of the Metalmarks family are almost invariably larger than the males and have broader wings, with males exhibiting a straighter costal and terminal margin on the forewing. Additionally, the long antennae (more than half the forewing length), which bears a slender, flattened club, help to distinguish the Metalmarks. They inhabit rocky hills, grassland, chaparral, and dunes. The upperside on the *A. mormo* is orange-brown to black, checkered with black and white spots. They have tan to brick-red patches on their forewing, and their undersides are gray with white spots. Males perch in hillside hollows to watch for females. Eggs are laid in groups of two to four on lower leaves of host plants, or singly on other parts of the plant. Caterpillars rest during the day in shelters of leaves tied together with silk, emerging at night to feed. Young caterpillars feed on leaves, older caterpillars eat leaves and stems.

The caterpillar is purple-grey and darker on the back.

male

female

Genus:
  Apodemia
Common names:
  Mormon Metalmark
Size:
  32 mm (1¼ in.)
Male or female specimen:
  Male and female
Locality:
  North Dakota (few) west to Washington, south through to southern California, Arizona, New Mexico
Host plants:
  Various wild buckwheats (*Eriogonum*)
Conservation status:
  Not protected

Apodemia · Nais

male

Description

The difference between the two sexes is the shape of the wings; the male has long, triangular wings, while the female's are rounded. Above, they are deep russet-orange with a faint grayish-brown cast, and both wings are profusely blotched with black squares and bars, forming three bands parallel to the margin which become haphazard nearer the body. The fringes are heavily checkered, and there is a short white dash along the forewing costa. Below, the forewing is a dull orange-yellow with black spots which are repeated. The hindwing is ivory-white, with a black capped orange spot row along the outer margin, and several orange patches, outlined in black, toward the base. The caterpillar is pale green, with bristles bunched into small clusters along the upper surfaces. There is one brood from June to early August, and occasionally May and September. Their habitat is brushy chaparral, foothills, and moister mountain canyons.

Genus:
  Apodemia
Common names:
  Nais Metalmark
Size:
  38 mm (1½ in.)
Male or female specimen:
  Male
Locality:
  Rocky Mountains from central Colorado south to New Mexico, Arizona and northern Sierra Madre Occidentale of Mexico
Host plants:
  Fendler's snowbrush (*Ceanothus fendleri*)
Conservation status:
  Not protected

Arcas · Imperialis

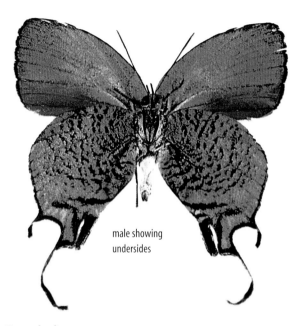

male showing undersides

Description

The very unique wing shape of these South American butterflies makes them very easy to identify. Unfortunately very little is known about their life cycle, or indeed their breeding host plants. The most remarkable feature of the *A. imperialis* are the two unequal length tails on the hindwings. The upperside is an amazing turquoise-green with a very distinct black tip and dot on the forewing. The undersides, as this picture shows, are bright green, which has a broken, mottled pattern in black on the hindwings.

Genus:
  Arcas
Common names:
  None
Size:
  38 mm (1½ in.)
Male or female specimen:
  Male (underside)
Locality:
  South America
Host plants:
  Not documented
Conservation status:
  Not protected

Arhopala · Aurea

male

Description

The males of this Arhopala species have forewings with a rather acute apex, unlike the females who possess the usual characteristics in having rounded forewings. The male of *A. aurea* is a bright coppery-green above with a slight basal bluish scaling. The hindwing border is broad and irregular and the green scaling does not reach the termen. The female is purple-blue above, and both sexes have short stumpy tails with tornal green scales. The undersides are a mottled pattern made up of little circular spots evenly dispersed over the wings. It is a powerful flier and lives in lowland forests.

Genus:
Arhopala
Common names:
None
Size:
44 mm (1¾ in.)
Male or female specimen:
Male
Locality:
South America
Host plants:
Not documented
Conservation status:
Not protected

Atlides · Halesus

male

Genus:
  Atlides
Common names:
  Great Purple Hairstreak
Size:
  38 mm (1½ in.)
Male or female specimen:
  Male
Locality:
  Guatemala north to central California, east
  through Texas and southern Missouri to
  Maryland
Host plants:
  Mistletoe (*Phoradendron* species) growing
  on several tree species
Conservation status:
  Not protected

Description

Great Purple Hairstreaks inhabit oak woods, mesquite forests, planted walnuts in agricultural or suburban areas, and mixed woods infested with mistletoe. The hindwing has one short and one long tail. The abdomen is blue on top, and a red-orange beneath. The upperside is black with widespread iridescent blue. The underside is black with iridescent gold markings near the tails. Males perch on treetops or other tall objects in the afternoon, watching for receptive females. Caterpillars eat leaves and male flowers of the host plant. Chrysalids hibernate in crevices at the base of the host tree or under loose bark. They have three flights from March to December. The adult butterflies feed on the nectar from flowers including goldenrod, Hercules club, shepherd's needle, sweet pepperbush, and wild plum.

male showing underside

Axiocerses · Amanga Mendeche

Description

This is a small tailed hairstreak which loves bright sunny areas. It lives in the bush and savannah where it breeds on a tropical oleacaceous plant called *Ximenia*. The male is a very vivid scarlet, and the female is not so bright and more orange-brown in color. Both the sexes have brown sections on the forewing tips, and also on the base of the thick-tailed hindwing. Very little is documented about the life cycle of this little butterfly.

Genus:
Axiocerses
Common names:
Bush Scarlet
Size:
35 mm (1⅜ in.)
Male or female specimen:
Male
Locality:
South America
Host plants:
Ximenia, tropical oleacaceous plant
Conservation status:
Not protected

Brephidium · Exilis

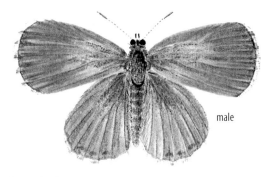

male

Description

This smallest western butterfly is abundant, but usually passes unnoticed because of its diminutive size and slow flight. Despite its minuteness and seeming fragility, the Western Pygmy-blue emigrates northward each year from its year-round southern homeland. They are bicolored above, and white-fringed, chocolate-brown with ultramarine blue inward. The female is slightly larger than the male and is less blue. The underside is a gray-brown, blending to bluish-gray at the base. There are tiny iridescent blue-green centered black spots on the hindwing margin, and white striations across the wings. The caterpillar is pale green to cream-white, with yellow stripes on the back and sides, and tiny brown "pimples" all over. These butterflies inhabit lowland, often disturbed places and coastlines; washes, marshes, alkali flats, railroad tracks, and vacant lots.

Genus:
Brephidium
Common names:
Western Pygmy-Blue
Size:
10 to 19 mm (⅜ to ¾ in.)
Male or female specimen:
Male
Locality:
Central California east to southern Nevada, central Arizona, central New Mexico and west Texas. South through southern California, Baja California and Mexico to Venezuela
Host plants:
Pigweed (*Chenopodium album*), saltbush species (*Atriplex*) and others in the goosefoot family (*Chenopodiaceae*)
Conservation status:
Not protected

male showing underside

Celastrina · Ladon

female

male

male showing underside

Calephelis · Borealis

male

male showing undersides

Description

These small butterflies overwinter in the pupal form, and are often among the earliest to emerge from the chrysalis in the spring. The color of the Spring Azure changes seasonally. For the most part, the upperside of the male's wings are blue, while the female's wing has some black on the forewing's outer edge. The underside of the hindwing is a grayish-white with faded small black dots, and margins in the center. Males are very active perching and patrolling for females from mid-afternoon until dusk. The eggs of the female are laid on flower buds. The caterpillars which hatch feed on the flowers and fruits of their host plants and are tended by ants. The caterpillars form their chrysalids and hibernate.

Genus:
  Celastrina
Common names:
  Spring Azure
Size:
  19 to 32 mm (¾ to 1¼ in.)
Male or female specimen:
  Male and female
Locality:
  Alaska and Canada south of the tundra through most of the United States except the Texas coast, southern plains and peninsular Florida; south in the mountains to Columbia
Host plants:
  Dogwood (*Cornus florida*), New Jersey tea (*Ceanothus americana*), meadowsweet (*Spiraea salicifolia*) and Collinsia
Conservation status:
  Not protected

Description

The Northern Metalmark occurs in widely dispersed, local, sparse colonies and, like many metalmarks, they land on the undersurfaces of leaves, with wings held out flat. They favor dry, open woods and hilly meadows, especially shale and limestone outcroppings. They are a rather dingy orange-brown above with a wide central dark band bisecting both wings. It has a relatively indistinct, but uninterrupted line of metallic marks. The undersides are light yellow-orange, often flushed with red, with lead-gray spotting. The fringe areas are slightly checkered. Caterpillars have long white hairs that grow upward and outward.

Genus:
  Calephelis
Common names:
  Northern Metalmark
Size:
  25 to 32 mm (1 to 1¼ in.)
Male or female specimen:
  Male
Locality:
  Western Connecticut south through west-central Pennsylvania; central Appalachians and Ohio River Valley
Host plants:
  Roundleaf ragwort (*Senecio obovatus*), possibly golden ragwort (*Senecio aureus*) and common fleabane (*Erigeron philadelphicus*).
Conservation status:
  Not protected

Calephelis · Virginiensis

male   male showing underside

Description

Distributed sporadically in all of the Gulf States, the Little Metalmark becomes progressively more local to the North. It is especially fond of pine flats, woodland edges, and damp habitats. It inhabits open grassy fields, pine savannah, salt marsh meadows, and wood margins. The male is a deep burnt orange with many irregular scalloped bands of bluish black, a regular curving submarginal band of silvery white bordered in black, and a similar zigzagging band near the center of the wing above. The female is a lighter shade above. Both are light orange with black speckling on the underside. They have three broods a year in mid-Atlantic states—May, July, and September. Individual broods less defined farther south; but every month in Florida.

Genus:
  Calephelis
Common names:
  Little Metalmark
Size:
  13 to 19 mm (½ to ¾ in.)
Male or female specimen:
  Male
Locality:
  Atlantic coastal plain from Maryland south to Florida and the Keys; west along the Gulf coast to southeast Texas
Host plants:
  Yellow thistle (*Cirsium horridulum*)
Conservation status:
  Not protected

Callophrys · Avis

Description

This butterfly is from a genus of small butterflies that have a striking green underside. The male has a darker upperside and its forewing apices are more acute. It is usually found in woodland scrubs and settles with its wings shut to preserve its camouflage. A close relation, and very similar in appearance, The Green Hairstreak is commonly found in the UK.

Genus:
  Callophrys
Common names:
  Chapman's Green Hairstreak
Size:
  33mm (1⅜in)
Male or female specimen:
  Female
Locality:
  Palearctic region
Host plants:
  Arbutus
Conservation status:
  Not protected

Callophrys · Dumetorum

Genus:
Callophrys
Common names:
Coastal Green Hairstreak, Bramble
Green Hairstreak
Size:
22 to 30 mm (⅞ to 1⅛ in.)
Male or female specimen:
Female (underside)
Locality:
North America
Host plants:
Eriogonum latifolium and occasionally
deerweed (*Lotus scoparius*)
Conservation status:
Not protected

Description

The Bramble Green Hairstreak, is quite a common spring butterfly, and is often the only green hairstreak in the lush, low elevation forests of western Washington and Oregon. However, it occurs far to the South as well. On the uppersides they are gray to dark gray-brown, and the female often has some reddish-brown, especially over the outer half of her wings. The undersides are green, except for a gray-brown area of the forewing, which are punctuated by an interrupted row of small white spots. They have a small, stubby tail and inhabit wastelands, dry washes, rocky hills, chaparral, and moist foothill canyons.

Calycopis · Cecrops

male

male showing undersides

Description

The Red-banded Hairstreak breeds year round in Florida and lays its dimpled white eggs in leaf litter below their host plants. When they hatch the caterpillars are pale yellow, but as they age, they darken. The caterpillars are covered with brown hairs and have a blue green stripe down their backs. They feed on oaks, crotons, and wax myrtles. In chrysalis form they are brown with black mottling. Adults sip mud and are attracted to the nectar of the host plants as well as dogbanes, milkweeds, wild cherry, and sweet pepperbush. The upperside of this butterfly is brown, with a blue hindwing which has two tails. The underside is gray-brown with a white postmedian line which is edged with an orange-red. They prefer coastal hammocks, overgrown fields, and forest edges. They are a relatively small butterfly, and they tend to stay hidden unless disturbed. They rest and bask with their wings closed.

Genus:
Calycopis
Common names:
Red-banded Hairstreak
Size:
25 to 32 mm (1 to 1¼ in.)
Male or female specimen:
Male
Locality:
Southeastern United States from Long Island south through Florida, west through entire area to southeast Kansas, eastern Oklahoma and eastern Texas. Strays to eastern Nebraska, northern Illinois and Michigan
Host plants:
Fallen leaves of wax myrtle (*Myrica cerifera*), dwarf sumac (*Rhus copallina*), staghorn sumac (*R. typhina*) and several oaks
Conservation status:
Not protected

Chalceria · Heteronea

male

female

The caterpillar and chrysalis both bear strong resemblances to plant leaves.

chrysalis

Description

Common over most of their range, both male and female Blue Coppers frequent flowers, especially the blossoms of wild buckwheat. The male is bright blue on the upperside, outlined in black, fringed with white, and marked with dark wing veins. Females are grayish blue to golden brown on the upperside, fringed with white and marked with dark brown spots. Underneath, both sexes are white to yellowish white and marked with black spots on the forewing and possibly on the hindwing. The caterpillar is light gray-green and marked with very tiny white dots, giving it a frosty appearance. It is covered with silvery white, short hair. It has an average, full-grown length of ¾ in. (19 mm).

Genus:
Chalceria
Common names:
Blue Copper
Size:
25 to 32 mm (1 to 1¼ in.)
Male or female specimen:
Male and female
Locality:
This species ranges from southern British Columbia south to central California and southeast to northern Arizona and New Mexico. It also occurs through most of Idaho
Host plants:
Buckwheat
Conservation status:
Not protected

Chalceria · Rubidus

male

female

male showing
underside

Genus:
  Chalceria
Common names:
  Ruddy Copper
Size:
  25 to 32 mm (1 to 1¼ in.)
Male or female specimen:
  Male and female
Locality:
  This species ranges from southern
  British Columbia and Alberta south
  through the northwestern U.S. to
  central California, eastern Arizona and
  northern New Mexico, and east as far
  as western North and South Dakota
  and Nebraska
Host plants:
  Rumex spp.
Conservation status:
  Not protected

Description

This is a medium-sized butterfly, which occurs in open areas such as sagebrush steppe, prairies, fields, and along streams.

The male is bright coppery orange on the upperside, lightly marked with dark spots and edged thinly in black. The female varies in color from golden yellow to dark brown clouded with yellow; the wings are marked with dark spots, and the hindwing has a golden yellow wavy band just in from the edge. Underneath, both sexes are yellowish gray to grayish white. The underside of the forewing is spotted with black while the underside of the hindwing may be unmarked or lightly dotted with black. Eggs overwinter and hatch in the spring, and the resulting brood is the only generation of caterpillars each summer. Each caterpillar undergoes four stages of growth, called instars. Adults generally fly from the end of May to the beginning of September. These butterflies are swift fliers, and may be spotted chasing each other.

Cheritra · Orpheus

Description

This is a magnificent butterfly that occurs in the Philippines. Its uppersides are a powerful orange-brown, with a very long pointed tail. In between the veins are dark scales which help to make the orange veins more prominent. At the base of the tail is an area of dark brown. Very little has been documented about the life cycle of this specimen.

Genus:
Cheritra
Common names:
None
Size:
41 mm (1⅝ in.)
Male or female specimen:
Male
Locality:
Philippines
Host plants:
Not documented
Conservation status:
Not protected

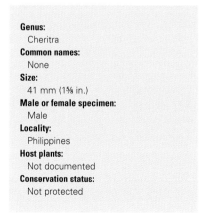

Cupido · Minimus

Description

The female of the Little Blue butterfly is completely black, whereas the male has a light dusting of blue scales. A local species in the United Kingdom, it is quite widespread throughout Europe. The Little Blue lives in small close-knit colonies. Most colonies consist of a few teams of adults which fly and breed in the same few square meters of ground year after year. Emigration occurs only if the habitat has become unsuitable. This is the most secretive of the blues that occur in Britain. The sexes are very slightly different, but both have brown upper surfaces. It is only the male that has a blue dusting of scales at the base of the wings. The undersides are very pale in contrast, a light gray that is speckled with small black dots.

Genus:
Cupido
Common names:
Little Blue, Small Blue
Size:
24 mm (⅞ in.)
Male or female specimen:
Male
Locality:
Europe and Asia
Host plants:
Kidney vetch (*Anthyllis vulneraria*)
Conservation status:
Not protected

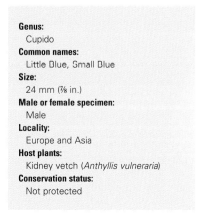

Cyanophrys · Crethona

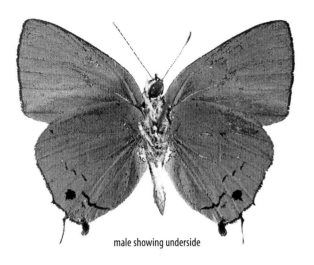

male showing underside

Description

This is the largest of the green hairstreaks that occurs in the West Indies. It is quite unmistakable because of its green undersides, and the pair of unequal length tails on the hindwing. The upperside of the male is bright blue, while those of the female are much more dull. It frequents lowland habitats and can only be found in Jamaica. Very little is known about its life cycle and its host plants.

Genus:
  Cyanophrys
Common names:
  Jamaican Green Hairstreak
Size:
  24 mm (1⁵/₁₆ in.)
Male or female specimen:
  Male (underside)
Locality:
  Jamaica
Host plants:
  Not documented
Conservation status:
  Not protected

Deudorix · Antalus

Description

This butterfly inhabits bushy hilltops, and the pupae feed on various tropical fruits. The female of the species is slightly larger than the male, and has rounded wings. They both have a blue-brown upperside, but there is a visible coppery sheen in the male which gives rise to the common name of Brown Playboy. Both the undersides of the male and female are similar, being white with just a few delicate lines crossing the wings. They have a small tail with two quite distinct white dots at the base.

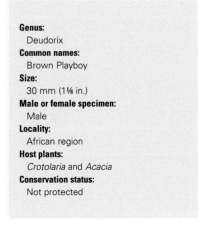

Genus:
  Deudorix
Common names:
  Brown Playboy
Size:
  30 mm (1⅛ in.)
Male or female specimen:
  Male
Locality:
  African region
Host plants:
  Crotolaria and *Acacia*
Conservation status:
  Not protected

Epidemia · Helloides

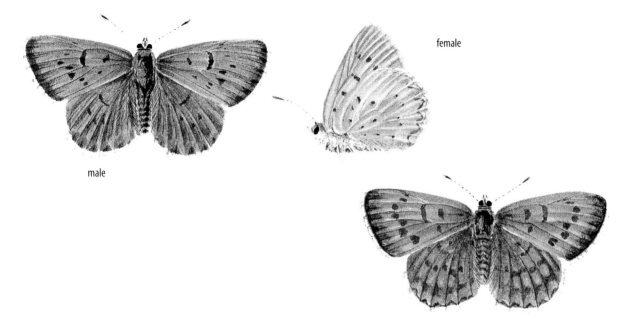

female

male

Genus:
  Epidemia
Common names:
  Purplish Copper
Size:
  25 to 32 mm (1 to 1¼ in.)
Male or female specimen:
  Male and female
Locality:
  Widespread in southern British
  Columbia, ranges east to the Great
  Lakes and south through the Midwest
  and Great Plains to Baja, California
Host plants:
  Buckwheats (*Rumex* spp., *Polygonum*
  spp.)
Conservation status:
  Not protected

Description

The upperside of the male is copper-brown with a purplish iridescence and scattered black spots. The female is more orange with brown margins and darker spots. The underside in both sexes is a dull pinkish-tan to grayish-tan with fine black spots and a scalloped red submarginal band. Whitish eggs are scattered at the base of the host plant or in litter beneath it. The caterpillar is green with oblique yellow marks on its sides and longitudinal yellow stripes on its back and sides. There are two broods in Canada, the first flying in June and July, with the second flying in August and September. They tend to frequent wet meadows, marshes, streamsides and disturbed areas such as open fields, and roadsides.

Epidemia · Mariposa

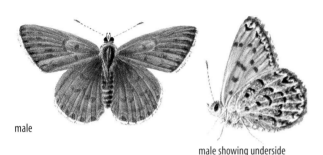

male

male showing underside

Description

This butterfly is fairly small to medium-sized, whose preferred habitat includes forest bogs and openings. The male is coppery brown on the upperside with a purplish sheen, and it is marked with pale brownish spots and crescents. The female is yellowish orange on the upperside of the forewings, marked with dark brown spots and light brown along the outside edge and near the body. The hindwing is mostly brown and marked with zigzag lines of yellowish orange. Underneath, both sexes are peach to grayish orange on the forewing, edged with brown and spotted with black. The underside of the hindwing is mottled grayish white to dark gray and marked with thin black crescents, curving toward the body. A very dark form is reported to occur in northern Idaho at low elevation. Eggs overwinter and hatch in the spring, and the resulting brood of caterpillars is the only one each year. Adults generally fly from July through September. It is not uncommon to observe large numbers of adults in a given area. The word *mariposa* is Spanish for "butterfly."

Genus:
Epidemia
Common names:
Mariposa Copper
Size:
25 to 32 mm (1 to 1¼ in.)
Male or female specimen:
Male
Locality:
This species ranges from southern Alaska south through British Columbia and Alberta, through the Pacific Northwest east to central Montana and Wyoming and south into northcentral California. In Idaho, it occurs primarily in the northern and central sections of the state
Host plants:
Heath family (*Ericaceae*), such as huckleberry (*Vaccinium* spp.) or on plants belonging to the buckwheat family (*Polygonaceae*)
Conservation status:
Not protected

Estemopsis · Inaria Thyatira

Description

This is a Metalmark butterfly that inhabits the Amazon rainforest. The male is extremely colorful with a brown background and an amazing wedge of brick-red on both the forewing and most of the hindwing. The female, in comparison, has markings of yellow-brown on its upperside. Very little is known of the life history of this butterfly.

Genus:
Estemopsis
Common names:
None
Size:
38 mm (1½ in.)
Male or female specimen:
Male
Locality:
South America
Host plants:
Not documented
Conservation status:
Not protected

Euphilotes · **Enoptes**

male

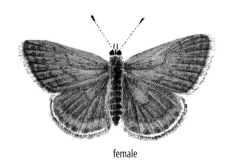

female

male showing
underside

Genus:
Euphilotes
Common names:
None
Size:
38 mm (1½ in.)
Male or female specimen:
Male
Locality:
Western United States from
Washington south through Pacific
Coast states to northern Baja
California. Also Nevada and northwest
Arizona
Host plants:
Various *Eriogonum* species including
Nude Buckwheat, Wright's Buckwheat,
Inflated Buckwheat, and others
Conservation status:
Not protected

Description

The Dotted Blue is geographically variable. The upperside of the male is lilac blue with dark borders, while the female is brown usually with an orange patch on the margin of the hindwing. The undersides of both sexes are off-white with black spots. Those on the forewing are larger and more squarish than those on the hindwing. There is also an orange band on the hindwing, which is usually broken into separate spots. Dotted Blues usually stay near their host plants. Males patrol around the host plants all day to find females. Eggs are laid singly on flowers or buds, and the caterpillars eat flowers and fruits and are tended by ants. There is one flight from mid-May to October depending on host and location.

Eurybia · Juturna Hari

Genus:
  Eurybia
Common names:
  None
Size:
  64 mm (2½ in.)
Male or female specimen:
  Male (underside)
Locality:
  South America
Host plants:
  Not documented
Conservation status:
  Not protected

Description

These dark-colored South American metalmarks live in the Amazon basin but are hardly ever seen. Their distinctive markings are made up of orange and brown and in this species the orange is crossed by two rows of dark brown spots. The eyespots on the female forewing are surrounded by a thicker orange line, and there is also a scattering of small orange spots covering the brown wings.

Everes · **Amyntula**

male

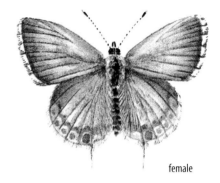

female

Genus:
Everes
Common names:
Western Tailed Blue
Size:
19 to 32 mm (l to 1¼ in.)
Male or female specimen:
Male and female
Locality:
Alaska south to Baja California and Mexico, east across Canada to N. central states and south in Rockies to Arizona and New Mexico
Host plants:
Legumes with inflated pods including false lupine (*Thermopsis*), milkvetch (*Astragalus*), crazyweed (*Oxytropis*) and vetches (*Vicia* and *Lathyrus*)
Conservation status:
Not protected

Description

As they drink, Tailed Blues twitch their hindwings in a way that calls attention to their threadlike tails, possibly distracting predators from attacking the body. Above they are a bright lavender-blue with a very narrow dark margin. The female is more brown and black than blue. The undersides are chalk-white, with an irregular band of black spots, and an indistinct submarginal band of darker gray and an orange-and-black patch near the middle of the outer margin on the hindwing. They like moist meadows, canyons, and can also be seen along roadsides, sandy clearings, and forest margins.

male showing underside

Glaucopsyche · Lygdamus

male

male showing underside

Genus:
 Glaucopsyche
Common names:
 Silvery Blue
Size:
 19 to 32 mm (I to 1¼ in.)
Male or female specimen:
 Male
Locality:
 Central Alaska south to southern California, Baja California, Arizona, New Mexico and western Kansas. Along northern United States east to Nova Scotia and south to Georgia
Host plants:
 Astragalus, Lotus, Lupinus, Melilotus, Oxytropis, Lathyrus, Vicia and other species in the pea family
Conservation status:
 Not protected

Description

The Silvery Blue can be found in a variety of locations including open woods, coastal dunes, prairies, meadows, road edges, rocky moist woods, and brushy fields. The male is blue with sporadic silver tinting and a white-and-gray border. The female is darker above. Both are gray on their undersides with an irregular band of distinct black, white-edged dots on each wing and a thin, submarginal band of white. There is one flight from March to June at low elevations, June-August at high elevations. Males patrol near the host plants for females. Eggs are laid singly on flower buds and young leaves of the host plants.

The winter months are spent in chrysalis stage, which is light brown with black spots. The caterpillar (left) is often attended by ants and is easily found by locating large assemblies of ants on host plants.

Harkenclenus · Titus

female

male

Genus:
Harkenclenus
Common names:
Coral Hairstreak
Size:
25 to 32 mm (1 to 1¼ in.)
Male or female specimen:
Male and female
Locality:
Central Canada south to eastern
California; east across southern Canada
to New England; south to central New
Mexico, central Texas, northern
Arkansas and central Georgia
Host plants:
Wild cherry, wild plum and chokecherry
(*Prunus* species) in the rose family
(*Rosaceae*)
Conservation status:
Not protected

Description

Hairstreaks are smallish butterflies, and are typically blue, brown, or gray, but can be many other colors. Hairstreaks get their name from a thin, hairlike tail that projects from the back of the hindwing. Supposedly, this acts to distract predators, which attack the tail. The Coral Hairstreak, however, is one of a few hairstreaks that does not have the tail. The male is brown with red orange patches in an irregular band along the margin of the hindwing above. The female is a lighter brown with less distinct red orange patches. Both are gray-brown with a band of black, white-edged patches in an irregular band across the middle of both wings, and a red orange band edged with white and black near the outer margin of the hindwing below. The caterpillar is green with a pink patch on its back and appears very soft.

Hemiargus · Isola

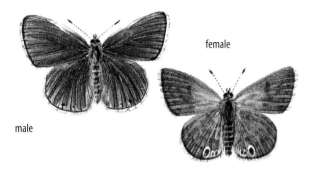

female

male

Description

Largely inhabiting the American Tropics, Reakirt's Blue becomes much rarer and more sparsely distributed to the North and East. Resident southern populations invade the North annually in highly variable numbers, depending on climate and other conditions. Although they persist well into fall, these blues lack the ability to overwinter in the North, and they die back each year. Because they tend to be loners, they are sometimes called "Solitary Blues." The male is light blue with a sporadic dusting of white; there are black borders along the outer edges and a black dot near the rear of the hindwing above. The female is light blue at the body, fading into gray-brown, with a white-blue border and a black, white-edged dot near the rear of the hindwing above. Both are pale gray-brown below with a distinct band of black; and white-edged spots near the middle of the forewing.

Genus:
   Hemiargus
Common names:
   Reakirt's Blue, Solitary Blue
Size:
   19 to 32 mm (I to 1¼ in.)
Male or female specimen:
   Male and female
Locality:
   Southern California, the Southwest and
   Texas through Mexico and Central
   America to Costa Rica
Host plants:
   Many plants in the pea family
   (*Fabaceae*) including yellow sweet
   clover (*Melilotus officinalis*), rattleweed
   (*Astragalus*), mesquite (*Prosopis*),
   indigo bush (*Dalea*), mimosa (*Albizia*)
   and indigo (*Indigofera*) species
Conservation status:
   Not protected

Heodes · Alciphron

female   male

Description

This butterfly comes from a genus of very brightly colored coppers which are dimorphic, having typically copper-colored males and speckled females. They frequent open, flowery places, often in mountainous regions, and occur in Europe and Asia. The Purple-shot Copper gets its name from the magnificent purple-shot iridescence on the forewings. The female is brown with an orange band running along the margin of the hindwing. The undersides of both sexes are similar, and there is an orange-gray glow that is speckled with black spots, and a repeat of the orange band on the hindwing.

Genus:
   Heodes
Common names:
   Purple-shot Copper
Size:
   32 mm (1¼ in.)
Male or female specimen:
   Male
Locality:
   Europe and Asia
Host plants:
   Rumex species
Conservation status:
   Not protected

Hyllolycaena · *Hyllus*

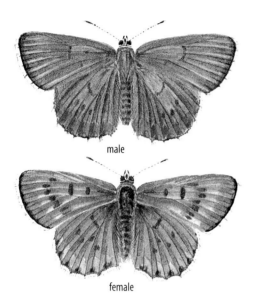

male

female

Genus:
Hyllolycaena
Common names:
Bronze Copper
Size:
32 to 38 mm (1¼ to 1½ in.)
Male or female specimen:
Male and female
Locality:
Maine west across southern Canada and the Great Lake states to eastern Montana and central Colorado; south to Arkansas, Mississippi, West Virginia and Maryland
Host plants:
Herbs of the buckwheat family (*Polygonaceae*) including curly dock (*Rumex crispus*)
Conservation status:
Not protected

Description

These butterflies frequent open wet meadows with *Polygonum* or *Rumex*, pond margins, marshes, usually with neutral to alkaline soil pH. The upperside of the male is an iridescent copper-brown with submarginal purple shading and a broad, irregular band of orange along the rear of the hindwings. The female is a brighter orange to yellow above. Both sexes are gray-white and pale orange with black spots below. Males perch on low growth near host plants to watch for females. She lays her eggs singly on plants, where they hibernate until spring. The caterpillar is green with a dark line along its back.

Hypaurotis · Chrysalus

Description

The Colorado Hairstreak butterfly adopted as the official state insect on April 17, 1996. The wings are pale blue bordered by olive with a few orange spots above. Below they are a brownish gray with a bluish hint and two narrow white and black bands. They are relatively easily identified by a slender tail that protrudes from the hind wing and their spectacular coloration. Adults fly once a year and rest on oak thickets and feeding on tree sap, raindrops and aphid honeydew.

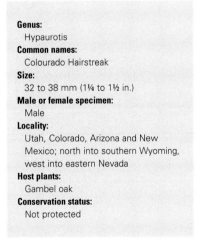

Genus:
Hypaurotis
Common names:
Colourado Hairstreak
Size:
32 to 38 mm (1¼ to 1½ in.)
Male or female specimen:
Male
Locality:
Utah, Colorado, Arizona and New Mexico; north into southern Wyoming, west into eastern Nevada
Host plants:
Gambel oak
Conservation status:
Not protected

Hypochrysops · Apollo

Description

The Apollo Jewel butterfly is found only where Ant-plants grow in northern Queensland which is where it pupates. The Ant plants are common to coastal swamps, paperbark and mangrove areas. It is known for its high degree of adaptation to its environment and for its exquisite coloring.

Genus:
Hypochrysops
Common names:
Apollo Jewel
Size:
36 mm (1⅜ in.)
Male or female specimen:
Male (underside)
Locality:
Australian region
Host plants:
Ant-plants (*Myrmecodia beccarii*)
Conservation status:
Not protected

Hypolycaena · **Philippus**

Description

The sexes of this species are fairly similar, and the The sexes of this species are fairly similar, and the common name is taken from the purple-brown color over the wings, albeit that it is very weak. This coloring is very typical of the species. The female is a little larger than the male, but both sexes have two unequal length tails. Their undersides are a pale white with three yellow, filigree-like lines crossing the wings. They prefer bushy habitat and the female lays her eggs on a member of the verbena family.

Genus:
Hypolycaena
Common names:
Purple-brown Hairstreak
Size:
30 mm (1⅛ in.)
Male or female specimen:
Male
Locality:
Africa (south of Sahara)
Host plants:
Verbena family (*Clerodendron*)
Conservation status:
Not protected

Icaricia · **Acmon**

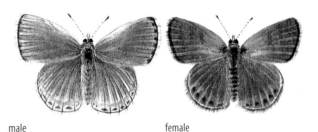

male   female

Description

The Acmon Blue can be seen in the desert, fields, prairie hills, weedy areas, and along roadsides, in fact wherever *Eriogonum fasciculatum* (Wild Buckwheat) grows. As these butterflies drink they twitch their hindwings, and in so doing, flash their emerald scales in the sunshine, making them quite a spectacular sight. The male is dark blue with a scalloped band of orange and black along the rear of the hindwing on the upperside. The female is brown with blue only near the body. Both sexes are very similar on the undersides; off-white to pale gray with several irregular rows of black spots across the wings, a band of U-shaped orange, and black-edged patches submarginally across the hindwing. This highly adaptable and efficient colonizer is one of the most widespread and common blues in the west of America. Early spring females in the lowlands have extensive blue scaling on the dorsal wing and are referred to as form *cottlei*. Later brood females are usually brown on the dorsal wing with no evidence of blue.

Genus:
Icaricia
Common names:
Acmon Blue, Emerald-studded Blue, Silver-studded Blue
Size:
25 mm (1 in.)
Male or female specimen:
Male and female
Locality:
Primarily California west of Sierra Nevada-Cascade Divide south to northern Baja California
Host plants:
Buckwheat, locoweed, knotweed and lupine
Conservation status:
Not protected

Iolaus · Timon Congoensis

Description

This butterfly has one of the longest tails of any species, being about equal to the length of the hindwing in some specimens. On each hindwing there is a pair of unequal length tails. They frequent open, woody areas along forest margins, and also bush country. Their upperside is distinctively marked with an iridescent green over a black background, except the tails which are white. The undersides are completely different to the uppers, being white with only a few black marks toward the base of the tail.

Genus:
  Iolaus
Common names:
  Congo Long-tailed Blue
Size:
  45 mm (1¾ in.)
Male or female specimen:
  Male
Locality:
  Africa
Host plants:
  Mistletoe (*Loranthus*)
Conservation status:
  Not protected

Jacoona · Amrita

These butterflies occur from Burma through Malaya, where it inhabits open forest in lowland and upland areas. The female is more commonly spotted than the male. The image on the left shows the undersides of the female.

Description

The Grand Imperial is rare, and on Singapore island, usually it is only individuals that are observed. In the male, the upper surface is a shining blue with the apical areas black bordered. The female is dark brown above with black and white markings on the tornal area of the hindwings. On the undersides, the forewing and the costal half of the hindwing are orange, with the rest of the hindwings white with black markings. The species is remarkable in that its long white tails are usually as long as the fore- and hindwings.   The tails trail elegantly behind the butterfly as it flies. The Grand Imperial has recently been found at one of Singapore's offshore islands, Pulau Tekong, and apparently is quite common on the island, where up to five individuals were seen in one morning.   The female appears to be the commoner

Genus:
  Jacoona
Common names:
  Grand Imperial
Size:
  50 mm (2 in.)
Male or female specimen:
  Female (underside)
Locality:
  Asia
Host plants:
  Not documented
Conservation status:
  Not protected but quite rare

Leptotes · **Marina**

male

female

male showing underside

Genus:
Leptotes
Common names:
Marine Blue
Size:
19 to 25 mm (¾ to 1 in.)
Male or female specimen:
Male and female
Locality:
Southern California east through the Southwest, Mexico and Baja California to Guatemala. Wanders and temporarily colonizes north to Wisconsin, Indiana, Kentucky and Louisiana
Host plants:
Leadwort (*Plumbago*) and many legumes including alfalfa (*Medicago sativa*), milkvetch (*Astragalus*) and mesquite (*Prosopis*)
Conservation status:
Not protected

Description

The Marine Blue extends its range farther northward every summer, only to see its new territory lost as the colonists die off. The upperside of the male is blue with a purple tinge. The female is a mottled brown with some blue on the dorsal wing. Both sexes are patterned in alternating, irregular bands of tan, brown, and cream, with black spots near the outer angle of the hindwing on the undersides. Males patrol to find females, who lay their eggs singly on flower buds of the host plant. The caterpillars range from green to brown in coloration, and eat flowers and seedpods. The adult butterflies fly from April to September in the North, but all through the year in south Texas and southern California

Lycaena · Helloides

Description

The male and female Purplish Copper are distinctly different from each other, only the male, which is small and darker than the female, shows the purplish sheen when viewed at certain angles. They live in disturbed areas including roadsides and open fields, wet meadows, marshes, streamsides and valleys and breed on various members of the buckwheat family, such as docks and knotweeds. There appear to be three generations per year with perhaps a partial fourth in October.

Genus:
  Lycaena
Common names:
  Purplish Copper
Size:
  32 mm (1¼ in.)
Male or female specimen:
  Male
Locality:
  North America
Host plants:
  Knotweeds (*Polygonum*) and docks (*Rumex*) in the buckwheat family (*Polygonaceae*), cinquefoils in the rose family (*Rosaceae*)
Conservation status:
  Not protected

Lyropteryx · Apollonia

Description

The life history of this species of butterflies is not well documented and still remains a mystery. The sexes of *L. apollonia* are dimorphic, but they both share the same patterning. The rays on the male have a slight greenish tinge and start from halfway in each of the wings. The rays are much longer in the female and white in colour. She also has a unique orange border on the trailing edge of the hindwing. The undersides are quite different, with a black background which is broken up by a number of large red spots at the base, from which rays radiate out.

Genus:
  Lyropteryx
Common names:
  None
Size:
  50 mm (2 in.)
Male or female specimen:
  Male (underside)
Locality:
  Central America and Northern South America
Host plants:
  Not documented
Conservation status:
  Not protected

Lysandra · Hispana

Description

This is quite a widespread Mediterranean species although it is quite difficult to spot. It resembles the very common and widespread Chalk Hill Blue (*Lycaena coridon*) with which it flies. The *L. hispana* flies from mid-April to October. The sexes are dimorphic, the male being a pale silvery blue with a faint yellowish tinge and dark margins. The female, in contrast, is brown. Both the sexes have very pale undersides which are patterned with orange and black spots. They occur in flower meadows in southern France, Italy and Spain, but as yet there is no documented evidence of their host plants.

A pair of mating Provence Chalk-hill Blues

Genus:
   Lysandra
Common names:
   Provence Chalk-hill Blue
Size:
   36 mm (1⅜ in.)
Male or female specimen:
   Male
Locality:
   Europe
Host plants:
   Not known
Conservation status:
   Not protected

Maculinea · Alcon

Description

Maculinea alcon, or the Alcon Blue to give it its common name, is a butterfly found in Europe and Asia. Like other members of the genus *Maculinea*, it has a very unusual life cycle. Eggs are laid on certain foodplants on which the first three larval instars feed. However, the fourth instar leaves the plant, drops to the ground and is 'adopted' by an ant colony, where the caterpillar becomes a parasite of the ants. The male is a rich violet-blue colour, while the female is mainly black with an area of violet-blue at the base of the wings. Both of the sexes have a white fringe, but on the male it is edged in black. The undersides are beige, and have a number of black spots speckled on the surface.

Genus:
   Maculinea
Common names:
   Alcon Blue
Size:
   38 mm (1½ in.)
Male or female specimen:
   Male
Locality:
   Europe and Asia
Host plants:
   Gentiana pneumonanthe; larvae
   attended by ants *Myrmica ruginodis*
Conservation status:
   Not protected

Mesosemia · Hewigis

Description

This genus of butterflies can easily be identified by the very prominent eyespots which tend to give them a face-like appearance. Also, something which is quite unusual for a butterfly, is the fact that they tend to hop through vegetation rather than to fly. The undersides of *M. hewigis* have a large pupilled eyespot on the forewing and a thick white band which crosses over the brown wings. The base of the wing is a lighter shade of brown. Little is known about the life cycle of this metalmark from South America.

Genus:
  Mesosemia
Common names:
  None
Size:
  46 mm (1¾ in.)
Male or female specimen:
  Male
Locality:
  South America
Host plants:
  Not documented
Conservation status:
  Not protected

Methonella · Cecilia

Description

This South American butterfly has very distinctive scalloped hindwings. The male and female share the same basic pattern formation on their wings, but their colouring differs. The male is much brighter with a brilliant orange in the middle of each dark chocolate-coloured wing. The female, on the other hand, has a big area of pale yellow in the centre of the forewing and a much smaller area of orange in the middle of the wings. Very little is documented about the lifestyle of this butterfly.

Genus:
  Methonella
Common names:
  None
Size:
  38 mm (1½ in.)
Male or female specimen:
  Male
Locality:
  South America
Host plants:
  Not documented
Conservation status:
  Not protected

Ministrymon · Leda

Genus:
  Ministrymon
Common names:
  Leda Hairstreak, Mesquite
  Hairstreak
Size:
  22 mm (⅞ in.)
Male or female specimen:
  Male
Locality:
  Mexico and Baja California north
  into southern Arizona and southern
  California
Host plants:
  Mesquite trees (*Prosopis* species)
  in the pea family (*Fabaceae*)
Conservation status:
  Not protected

Description

The Leda Hairstreak is a very small butterfly which is strongly attracted to flowers. Late autumn individuals are a darker grey than those of earlier broods. This butterfly has two distinct forms, with and without red markings. This kind of dimorphism may be due to different seasonal conditions, such as moisture variation, or it may be a balanced, genetically fixed set of frequencies within the population. Although the exact cause of the dimorphism remains uncertain, lepidopterists know that the two forms definitely belong to the same species because eggs of one have produced the other.

Both sexes are similar in appearance. Above they are blue at the base, and grey-black over the greater part of the forewing. The undersides are grey crossed by a jagged black postmedian line with or without a red outline. A black-centred red spot and blue patch may or may not be present near the two tails, and there are faint spots at the base of the wing.

Mitoura · Gryneus

male

male showing underside

Genus:
  Mitoura
Common names:
  Olive Hairstreak
Size:
  19 to 32 mm (¾ to 1¼ in.)
Male or female specimen:
  Male
Locality:
  East: New England west to Nebraska, south to Florida and Texas. West: Montana, North Dakota and Nebraska south to southern California, Arizona, New Mexico and Baja California
Host plants:
  Southern Red Cedar (*Juniperus virginiana*)
Conservation status:
  Not protected

Description

This butterfly is completely dependent on the southern red cedar, its sole larval host, and requires intact stands of mature trees to maintain a viable colony. Adults have a rapid, somewhat erratic flight and spend most of their lives residing high up on host branches. This somewhat sedentary behaviour and preference for location often makes detection difficult. The male is brown with a tint of orange and darker margins above. The female has more orange above. Both are brilliant green with an irregular band of white and brown, and an evenly spaced, broken band of white along the forewing margin below. The Olive Hairstreak flourishes in new, early woodland growth of abandoned agricultural areas, but declines as later stages of regrowth starts to take place.

The caterpillar is green with lighter lines along its sides. The winter months are spent in the brown chrysalis stage (left).

Mitoura · Spinetorum

male

Description

The Thicket Hairstreak is a small but somewhat stunning looking butterfly. It has a blue top, while the underside is brownish with a stark white line. You can see a sort of 'w' on the hindwing of the white line. It inhabits pinyon-juniper forests, mixed woodland and coniferous forests, where the males perch in tall trees to find receptive females. She lays her eggs singly on mistletoe and caterpillars eat all external parts of it. Chrysalids hibernate in the mistletoe mass. They have one flight from May to August. Males of the Thicket Hairstreak claim territories along hilltops and canyon ridges, where mating takes place. The caterpillar is green with patches of red and white, and many 'pimples'. The winter months are spent in the grey-brown chrysalis stage.

Genus:
Mitoura
Common names:
Thicket Hairstreak
Size:
25 to 32 mm (1 to 1¼ in.)
Male or female specimen:
Male
Locality:
British Columbia southeast through the Rocky Mountains to New Mexico and into Mexico; south through California into Baja California
Host plants:
Dwarf mistletoes (*Arceuthobium* species), in the *Loranthaceae* family, which grow on juniper, pine and fir trees
Conservation status:
Not protected

male showing underside

Myrina · Dermaptera

Description

The Lesser Figtree Blue belongs to a genus of African butterflies which live in the savanna and wooded country where their host plants, fig, are abundant. They are sexually dimorphic, and both the male and female have reasonably long tails. The male is predominantly royal blue with the apex of the forewing being black. There are also some black marginal and vein markings on the hindwing. The female is considerably larger and is more black with less of the prominent blue. In both sexes the undersides are grey with an orange and white eyespot on the hindwing at the base of the spatulate tail.

Genus:
Myrina
Common names:
Lesser Figtree Blue
Size:
35 mm (1⅜ in.)
Male or female specimen:
Male
Locality:
Africa
Host plants:
Fig (*Ficus*)
Conservation status:
Not protected

Necyria · Bellona

male

Description

This metalmark has colourful iridescent markings. They can be seen flitting around the forest margins and tend to mimic other forest butterflies. The *N. bellona* is a metallic black but with a slight blue-green iridescence. The male has a black background colour and its forewings are quite distinctly pointed. There is a red band which crosses over just half of the blue-black hindwing. The female has a noticeably blue dusting over her basic black background especially towards the edges of the wings, and she also has a thin red band on both the forewing and hindwing. This butterfly is found mainly in Bolivia.

Genus:
 Necyria
Common names:
 None
Size:
 50 mm (2 in.)
Male or female specimen:
 Male (underside)
Locality:
 South America
Host plants:
 Fig (*Ficus*)
Conservation status:
 Not protected

below: Necyria Manco
The colour scheme of this butterfly seems to be quite common in the rainforests and is very similar to the Lyropteryx. There does appear to be a certain amount of mimicry between the species.

Ogyris · Genoveva Gela

Mature larvae (above) and pupae (below) with attendant ants Camponotus nigriceps.

Genus:
  Ogyris
Common names:
  Genoveva Azure
Size:
  64 mm (2½ in.)
Male or female specimen:
  Female
Locality:
  Australian region
Host plants:
  Mistletoe
Conservation status:
  Not protected

Description

This species occurs in Queensland, New South Wales, Victoria and South Australia and is prized by collectors. Not only this they are vulnerable to destruction of their natural forest habitats, where they breed on parisitic mistletoes. The male adult is metallic purple in colour. The female is black with metallic azure towards the hinge, and a cream patch near the tip of each forewing. The undersides of the forewings are dark brown, with a series of white bars along the costa. The hindwings underneath have a complex fawn pattern. The females have an additional white patch under each forewing. The caterpillar is flattened, and brown with darker brown dots. It lives in a nest of any of several species of Sugar Ants (*Camponotus*, *Formicinae*), and is shepherded to its food by the ants. The pupa is dark brown and formed in the ants' nest.

Parrhasius · M-album

male

male showing underside

DESCRIPTION

The White M Hairstreak gets its name from the white-bordered pattern below. A fast and erratic flier, it seems to be more abundant in the southeastern part of its range than further north or west. They frequent woods with broadleaf trees, and sip nectar from a variety of flowers including viburnum, sumac, sourwood, wild plum, poinsettia, sweet pepperbush, common milkweed, lantana, dogwood and goldenrod. They are long-tailed, and their uppersides are a bright iridescent blue with wide black margins. The male is brighter blue than the female with a forewing stigma. The undersides of both sexes have a thin, but prominent, white and black bordered postmedian band forming a distinct 'M' near the two hindwing tails. There is a prominent reddish spot and blue area near the tails. The caterpillar is a downy, light yellow-green, with a dark, dull green back stripe and slanting side bars. The mottled brown chrysalis overwinters, possibly in litter below host oak trees, (Quercus) which include live oak (Q. virginiana).

Genus:
  Parrhasius
Common names:
  White M Hairstreak
Size:
  30 mm (1⅛ in.)
Male or female specimen:
  Male
Locality:
  Connecticut west to southeast Iowa and Missouri, south to east Texas, the Gulf Coast and peninsular Florida. Rare stray to Michigan and Wisconsin
Host plants:
  Live oak (Quercus virginiana) and other oak species
Conservation status:
  Not protected

Plebejus · Saepiolus

male

female showing underside

Genus:
  Plebejus
Common names:
  Greenish Blue, Greenish Clover Blue
Size:
  30 mm (1⅛ in.)
Male or female specimen:
  Male and female
Locality:
  North America
Host plants:
  Clover
Conservation status:
  Not protected

The caterpillar varies in colour, from greenish, to greenish-white tinged with purplish at the ends, to reddish. It has a bumpy appearance, with each individual segment appearing fat. It reaches an average, full-grown length of 12 mm (H in.).

DESCRIPTION

These butterflies vary greatly in appearance between populations, the sexes and even from individual to individual. Typically, the male is silvery blue on the upperside, possibly tinged with green. The borders of the wings are black and fringed with white. The forewing may have a dark spot near the middle, and the hindwing may have a faint row of blackish dots at the rear. Underneath is greyish-white to grey, possibly bluish where the wings meet the body. Both the fore- and hindwings are dotted with black underneath; the hindwing may have one large spot and/or several small, orange spots. The female is brownish on the upperside, possibly with orange near the edge of the wings, or brownish with blue shading, sometimes extensive, where the wings attach to the body. The forewing may have a dark spot near the middle. The edges are black and fringed with white. Underneath is beige and marked similarly to the male. It can be found in moist areas such as bogs, meadows, grassy fields, open forests and along streams. Most commonly, it occurs above 6,000 ft. elevation. The caterpillar is equipped with a honey gland, also known as a dorsal nectary organ, which emits a sugary solution agreeable to ants. The ants feed on the solution and in turn protect the caterpillar from predators.

Poecilmitis · Chrysaor

Description

These South African butterflies are quite small for coppers, and the sexes tend to be fairly similar in appearance. The Golden Copper frequents hilly and mountainous areas and breeds on *Rhus* and *Zygophyllum*. It is a bright reddish-copper colour, with a black band around the forewing, along with small black spots over the surface of the wings. The hindwing is drawn out into a partial tail.

Genus:
  Poecilmitis
Common names:
  Golden Copper
Size:
  30 mm (1⅛ in.)
Male or female specimen:
  Male
Locality:
  South Africa
Host plants:
  Rhus and *Zygophyllum*
Conservation status:
  Not protected

Polyommatus · Icarus

Description

The Common Blue is a very small butterfly widely distributed throughout Europe and Asia, and particularly common to mainland Britain. It is likely to be found in open, sunny fields, clearings and meadows in lowlands. Two generations of this butterfly are produced each year and the larvae feeds on trefoil plant species such as Black Medick (*Medicago Lupulina*) and Birds-foot-trefoil (*Lotus Cornniculatus*). Males have striking blue upper wings, but females vary from blue to a more brownish colour

Genus:
  Polyommatus
Common names:
  Common Blue
Size:
  35mm (1⅜in)
Male or female specimen:
  Male
Locality:
  Europe and Asia
Host plants:
  Birds-foot-trefoil (Lotus corniculaus)
Conservation status:
  Not protected

Pseudophilotes · **Abencerragus**

It has the typical Pseudophilotes habit of cupping its wings half open when it settles, as can be seen from this photograph.

Genus:
Pseudophilotes
Common names:
False Baton Blue
Size:
22 mm (⅞ in.)
Male or female specimen:
Female (underside)
Locality:
North Africa and Europe
Host plants:
Thymus, Salvia, Medicago, Cleonia
Conservation status:
Not protected

Description

This is a species of North Africa and the southern Iberian Peninsula. In North Africa it is widespread but always local. It is usually found near water, particularly where there are trees and shrubs, for example around irrigated fields or in oases deeper into the desert. This small genus of butterflies is characterized by the chequered fringes on the edges of both wings. The upperside of the male is brown, with a blue and chequered margin. The female is basically black with a blue area on the base of the wings. The undersides of both sexes are more or less the same, being grey broken up by black spots. It frequents places where heather grows in abundance.

Rhetus · Arcius

Genus:
   Rhetus
Common names:
   Sword-tailed Beautymark
Size:
   40 mm (1½ in.)
Male or female specimen:
   Male
Locality:
   South America
Host plants:
   Not documented
Conservation status:
   Not protected

Description

This beautiful butterfly inhabits the almond tree (*Terminalia catappa*), although it is not its host plant. It has a noticeable sexual dimorphism – the male is a magnificent shining blue, while the female is predominantly black. It has black and white stripes on its upperside, giving it a rather zebra-like appearance. The superb tail is formed mainly from an elongated part of the hindwing. The tail is very brightly coloured with blue, black and a red spot. The female is very similar in appearance, but usually has less blue. Unfortunately there is very little information about the life history of this beautiful butterfly.

Satyrium · Saepium

male

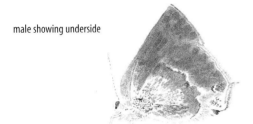

male showing underside

The brown chrysalis is extremely well camouflaged, resembling an animal dropping.

The larva is light green covered with short golden hairs. It has light stripes along the body and yellowish chevrons between the stripes.

Genus:
Satyrium
Common names:
Hedgerow Hairstreak
Size:
25 to 32 mm (1 to 1¼ in.)
Male or female specimen:
Male
Locality:
British Columbia south through California into Baja California; east through northern Arizona to northern New Mexico, Colorado and Montana
Host plants:
Ceanothus species in the buckthorn family (Rhamnaceae)
Conservation status:
Not protected

DESCRIPTION

This is a butterfly of drier mountain slopes and foothills, including brushy wooded areas where buckbrush occurs. The distinctive feature of this small Western Hairstreak is the bright coppery-brown colour of the upper surface of the wings. Markings on the dull brown underside are faint and irregular, but usually include a postmedian band and a blue spot on the margin of the hindwing. There is a short tail. The larvae of the Hedgerow Hairstreak is light green in colour with short yellow hairs, its body is marked with light stripes and yellow chevrons and feeds on host plant Ceanothus from the buckthorn family. It can be found around the western United States and British Columbia in Canada.

Satyrium · Calanus

male

Satyrium · Californica

male

Description

The Banded Hairstreak is the most common and widespread of our *Satyrium* hairstreaks, and is very similar to the ultra-rare Hickory Hairstreak. This butterfly likes to cling to low leaves and shrubs bathed in sunbeams and engages all newcomers in territorial tussles. Sometimes half a dozen may chase around together before settling. They can be found on their favourite nectar plants, such as milkweed, dogbane, daisies and sumac. The uppersides of this butterfly are a clouded black. Below, the male is dark brown and the female is grey-brown, with an irregular band of white and black double lines and a near margin band of white, black and orange (which is more pronounced near the tail on the hindwing).

Description

The California Hairstreak is a common sight along roadways and in dry areas in foothills and canyons, where the males often gather together. Each hindwing has one long and one short tail. The upperside is brown with orange spots on the hindwing near the tails. The outer edge of the forewing usually has a row of orange spots. The underside is a brownish-grey with orange submarginal crescents and a postmedian band of black spots. The caterpillar is a dull brown with white spots along its sides and grey spots on its back. The brown chrysalis has black patches and a green wing case.

Genus:
  Satyrium
Common names:
  Banded Hairstreak
Size:
  25 to 32 mm (1 to 1¼ in.)
Male or female specimen:
  Male
Locality:
  Maine across southern Canada to North Dakota; south to central Texas and the Gulf States. Southern Rocky Mountains in Wyoming, Colorado, Utah and New Mexico
Host plants:
  Many species of oak (*Quercus*), walnut (*Juglans*) and hickory (*Carya*)
Conservation status:
  Not protected

male showing underside

Genus:
  Satyrium
Common names:
  California Hairstreak
Size:
  25 to 32 mm (1 to 1¼ in.)
Male or female specimen:
  Male
Locality:
  British Columbia south to southern California and east to Colorado
Host plants:
  Amelanchier alnifolia, Prunus virginiana; Cercocarpus, Ceanothus, Quercus and *Salix* species
Conservation status:
  Not protected

Scolitantides · Orion Nigricans

left: Female Chequered Blue
The major part of the upperside of both wings is brown in colour with blue towards the base and a terminal fringe chequered brown and white. The underside of both wings is predominantly a pale grey-brown with brown and white patterns.

Genus:
Scolitantides
Common names:
Chequered Blue
Size:
32 mm (1¼ in.)
Male or female specimen:
Female
Locality:
Australian region
Host plants:
Saltbush
Conservation status:
Not protected

Description

The Chequered Blue earns its common name from the colour pattern along the outer margin of its wings. These butterflies are relatively small, and are present throughout the southern half of Australia. Adults can be seen flying almost all year round, except during June and July. The Chequered Blue is commonly found in a variety of habitats where the larval foodplants (saltbush) grow. They can be present in open woodland to open shrubland, mud flats, sand dunes and on inland saltbush plains. This species may also be very abundant in suburban areas, such as parks and gardens where various saltbush species have been planted. The caterpillars are green to grey-green in colour, enabling them to blend into the leaves of their foodplants. Due to their colouring the caterpillars are able to feed openly on the surface of the leaves both during the day and night. Caterpillars may also be attended by ants. The pupae can be found attached to the leaves and stems of the host plant.

Stalachtis · Calliope

Stalachtis Calliope (male)

Description

This species has mostly orange forewings with a black pattern made of longitudinal stripes at the base, large spots towards the middle and a band peppered with small white spots at the tip. The hindwing ground colour is black and there are a pair of long orange stripes in the middle and small white spots at the margin. The life history is unknown. *Stalachtis calliope* ranges widely in north and northeastern South America. In Peru it is found east of the Andes in the tropical rainforest. Both in colour and flight behaviour this generally common species mimics other species of butterflies in the Nymphalid subfamilies *Heliconiinae* and *Ithomiinae*, and its geographical colour variants each mimic different species. If disturbed the adults feign death.

Stalachtis Phaedusa (male)
This is a small butterfly in the same genus, and has the typical long rounded forewings of the rainforest metalmarks.

Genus:
　Stalachtis
Common names:
　None
Size:
　64 mm (2½ in.)
Male or female specimen:
　Male
Locality:
　South America
Host plants:
　Not documented
Conservation status:
　Not protected

Stalachtis Phlegia (male)
This is an easily identifiable metalmark from its speckled appearance, that inhabits the rainforests of Brazil.

Strymon · Melinus

male

The caterpillar of this species is also called the Cotton Borer because of the damage it has done to cotton crops in the South.

male showing underside

Genus:
  Strymon
Common names:
  Gray Hairstreak
Size:
  25 to 32 mm (1 to 1¼ in.)
Male or female specimen:
  Male
Locality:
  Throughout continental United States from southern Canada south to Mexico; southwards to Venezuela
Host plants:
  Pea (*Fabaceae*) and mallow (*Malvaceae*) families including beans (*Phaseolus*), clovers (*Trifolium*), cotton (*Gossypium*) and mallow (*Malva*)
Conservation status:
  Not protected

Description

This is a fairly small butterfly, with a thin tail extending from the rear of its hindwing. The upperside is dark grey to brownish-grey and marked with a single large orange spot on the rear of the hindwing near where the tail originates. The underside varies in colour from dark to light grey, and is marked with a thin, vertical line of black dashes, edged with white, running across both wings. The outer edge of both wings is marked similarly but more faintly. The underside of the hindwing is marked with one or two orange patches and two black spots at the rear. Males are marked along the sides of the abdomen with orange. It occurs in many kinds of open, often weedy, areas, including open woodlands, chaparral, along coasts and in fields and vacant lots.

The tails of the two hindwings of the butterfly resemble antennae and may act to fool predators into biting the wrong end of the butterfly allowing it to escape.

Thecla · Draudti

Female Thecla Draudti showing its underside

Thecla · Draudti

left: Thecla Telemus
This is a male specimen showing its underside which is a stunning green, blue, and red. This butterfly has three unequal tails which are slightly longer in the female.

Genus:
  Thecla
Common names:
  None
Size:
  42 mm (1⅝ in.)
Male or female specimen:
  Female (underside)
Locality:
  South America
Host plants:
  Not documented
Conservation status:
  Not protected

Description

T. draudti is a magnificent butterfly with a set of four tails, each one being a different length. It is quite large for a hairstreak, and the uppers are covered in a beautiful, iridescent metallic green. The underside by comparison is a wonderful array of colours – red, green, black and white. This butterfly can be found in Central America, but there is very little documented about its lifestyle or host plants.

Glossary of terms

abdomen – the rear part of the body which contains most of the gut and the reproductive organs.

aggregations – a term which applies mostly to caterpillars and adults which come together to feed or sleep.

anal region – the inside edge of the hindwing which is close to the tip of the abdomen. It is on the anal region of the hindwing that many key identification features are situated, such as eyespots, as well as various male characteristics.

androconial fold – a flap or fold on the inside edge of the hindwing adjacent to the abdomen, which contains the males' androconia, or androconial scales.

antenna(e) – the paired feelers on the head of an insect which are used for smell and touch.

apex – the tip of the forewing.

basking – a characteristic of some butterflies of either aligning themselves side-on to the sun, or sitting with wings open and flat on the ground or on a leaf, to absorb heat energy from the sun.

blues – members of the *Lycaenidae* to which blues, coppers and hairstreaks also belong.

browns – formerly members of the *Satyridae*, named after the general brown colours typical of most of the family, now included in *Nymphalidae*.

camouflage – the way in which butterflies and moths have colours and patterns which help them blend in with their background.

caterpillar – the stage after the egg, and before the chrysalis (pupa); the main eating stage during metamorphosis.

cell – an enclosed area of the forewing between the veins in which spots sometimes occur.

chevrons – a series of arrow-head marks around the edge of the wing, usually on the hindwing.

circumpolar – distribution of a butterfly within the arctic region around the North Pole.

claws – the end of each butterfly leg has one or two claws.

coppers – members of the *Lycaenidae* to which blues and hairstreaks also belong.

danaids – formerly members of the *Danaidae*, also known as the monarch or milkweed family, now included in *Nymphalidae*.

diapause – a period of reduced activity, typically found in pupae, usually to overcome inclement weather such as winter.

dimorphic – existing in two different forms; here applied to non-identical male and female butterflies of the same species.

dorsal – the topside of the body and wings.

emigrant – an insect which leaves one place for another place.

endangered – a species one step away from becoming extinct.

endemic – occurring only in a single region or locality.

extinct – not found in the wild for the past 50 years.

eyespots – spots of varying sizes on the upper or lower surface of the wings, which may or may not be pupilled and surrounded in various colours.

family – a major division of butterflies and moths.

form – an individual which differs from typical specimens in colour, pattern, shape or size; such as seasonal variation.

fringe – a fine edge of scales attached to the margin of the wing.

fritillaries – members of the *Nymphalidae* which are characterized by having an orange spotted pattern.

genus – the first word of the two-part Latin name given to a butterfly or moth.

gregarious – living together.

ground colour – the main colour of the butterfly which covers most of the wing; also called background colour.

habitat – a particular place whose characteristics are determined by the soil, vegetation and aspect.

heliconids – members of the *Nymphalidae* which are called longwings.

hibernation – a means of overcoming cold conditions by going into a resting stage.

immigrant – an insect which arrives in one place having come from another.

iridescence – the metallic appearance of some butterflies caused by light diffraction off the surface of the tiny scales which cover the wings.

lunules – a series of marks, often half-moon-shaped, which often forms a crescent inside the edge of the hindwing.

margin – the outer part of the wing.

metamorphosis – literally a change in form; there are four different life forms of a butterfly: egg, larva, pupa, adult.

migrant – an insect which moves from one area to another and back again.

mimic – an insect which evolves colour, pattern, shape of body, size and behaviour of another butterfly which it resembles.

mud-puddling – a term used to describe the male behaviour of visiting shallow puddles, animal droppings and the moist banks of rivers and streams to imbibe nutrients.

native species – a species which has evolved in one particular place or country.

nymphalids – members of the *Nymphalidae* which contains the aristocrats, browns, monarchs, *Libytheids*, *Nemeobiids* and glass wings.

osmaterium(a) – a bright orange, double filament produced by a swallowtail caterpillar when it is threatened.

oviposition – the act of laying eggs.

palps – paired sensory devices which are present around the mouth of the caterpillar and the butterfly.

patrolling – a behavioural characteristic of some butterflies, often males, which take up position in their own territory and patrol up and down to find mates.

polymorphism – existing in many forms.

predators – any organism, such as a spider, insect, lizard, bird or mammal, which preys upon another organism.

pupa(e) – the third stage in the complete metamorphosis.

rainforest – tropical forest which is described as either lowland or highland, depending on altitude.

resident – a butterfly which stays in the same locality from where it emerged until it dies.

satyrids – members of the *Nymphatidae* also called browns or satyrs.

sedentary – species which do not move around much.

setae – sensory hairs on the body of a caterpillar or butterfly.

snouts – butterflies which have long palps held out underneath and in front of the head.

species – a population of individuals which have fairly similar external characteristics, and which can mate amongst themselves to produce fertile offspring.

sphragis – a device which closes over the female abdomen after mating to stop any further mating, present in certain genera including *Parnassius*.

subspecies – an intermediary stage between one species evolving into another species.

sulfurs – members of the *Pieridae*.

taxonomy – the arrangement of species, genera and other groups into a system that denotes their relationship.

thorax – the middle section of the body which contains the flight muscles and wings, and from which the three pairs of legs originate, one pair from each of the three thoracic segments.

vagrant – an insect which occasionally moves from one place to another, but not with any regularity; the implication is that the movement is accidental.

variation – a natural feature displayed by all organisms; all their characteristics (visible and invisible ones) are subject to small changes within all members of the same species.

veins – the supporting structure of the wing; venation is critical in butterfly identification.

ventral – the underside of the body and wings.

whites – members of the *Pieridae*.

wingspan – twice the measurement from the centre of the thorax to the tip of the forewing. Usually the forewing measurement is taken as it is normally greater than that of the hindwing.

Index